A Man's Game

Sherene Mckoy

{NB: For creole translation, please see pages 281-288}

****

Published by:
Sherene Mckoy
Jamaica, WI
Email: authorsherenemckoy@gmail.com

Cover Design: Sherene Mckoy
Edited by: Shanique Shand
ISBN: 978-976-96465-0-6

Acknowledgements

"I can do all things through Christ which strengthens me" —Philippians 4:13

Compiling a book is a time-consuming project that requires a lot of dedication. The intricacies of the writing process require great attention because it entails the reconstruction of phrases and lines to create a perfect or almost perfect body of work. I could not have endured this process alone and as such, it would be remiss of me to not give credit where it's due. With that said, I wish to offer my sincere thanks to those who played their role in getting this book ready for the hearts and minds of the readers.

A special thanks to my nephew, Michael Robertson who was the first individual to set eyes on the content. He played a vital role in the first attempt to enhance the material, with specific focus on the flow of words and sentences.

Ms. Ruth Taylor (Author), thank you for taking the time to point me in the right direction to get my book ready for the market. You and your team went through the book to ensure it was appealing to readers.

Without mentioning names, I wish to thank any other person (friends, family, and acquaintances) who was instrumental in the preparation and publishing of this book. Words cannot express my gratitude for your immeasurable moral and emotional support through encouraging words, prayers and expressions of expectancy concerning this book. May God bless you richly for pouring into my life while I endure this tedious process.

Finally, I wish to extend gratitude to God for equipping me with the strength and resilience to persevere to the end. His Word in Phillipians 1:6, "And I am certain that God, who began the good work within you, will continue his work until it is finally finished on the day when Christ Jesus returns" is an assurance that He is with me. I am a work in progress, but He still calls me worthy of this assignment. Without Him, I would be nothing.

Introduction

A Man's Game chronicles the story of four women who fell for *his* games. Each story leaves every woman wondering what she could have done differently. It tells of the many battles a woman faces as she tries to see the best in her partner. It shows how easily she can become heartbroken in trying to hold on to a world which is being ripped from beneath her, while the next prey is being hunted by the predator. You will gain insight into his mind and his world. Learn our (women's) stories through their (men's) games.

Let's look at what so many women have experienced with men whom vowed to protect them. For those of us who believe that our experience and voice must be kept silent, our stories will be told through these words.

I have yet to see any law, rule or scientific evidence that can ably assist in the explanation of a man's behavior. It is thought by our beloved psychologists that every person carries a different identity gene, and so the behavior of every individual is different. If so, how can we then explain the reason it has become so easy for some males to behave similarly? Many of them seem to be synchronized when it comes to the way they speak, act or even make decisions, as well as the mindset they have when they believe their happiness is threatened.

Women will be left to decide if some men carry a huge chip on their shoulders or glorify themselves by playing the part of the abuser, inflicting wounds on any woman who dares to give a caring glance or verbalize her commitment. Too many men tend to expect so much yet give so little in return. Their behavior is that of a well-devised plan which will help them to achieve their main goal: Dominance.

To be fair, our men do deserve credit because there are good men around. However, some have not grasped the concept of manhood and what it truly entails, especially concerning a woman. Like everything, there is a good and bad side and while there are those men who aim to preserve and protect, there are those who wreck that which has been entrusted in their care. This book is about exposing the ugly truths and their devastating effects on women and is not a deliberate attack against men.

Men, your games may never end, but our stories must be told. Some tales will be told because the truth has been revealed, some will be left unspoken due to unanswered questions, and some will spark your desire to start at the beginning. Two things which cannot be denied are that whatever effect these stories might have on you, we can all relate, and we all have our own story to tell.

TABLE OF CONTENTS

She dark rose

He tempted her with lies,
And honeyed excuses,
Just to drink her slowly,
Because she was soft and weak.
Desperate for his affection.
He finished her smoothly,
Leaving, only tears,
Dripping from her penetrated soul,

A Man's Game

Shattered memories of love,
Lay wasted on the floor,
An unforgiving gore,
Of man's betrayal.
   —Michael Robertson

******

Let's take a look into A Man's Game...

1.

The Silent Spouse

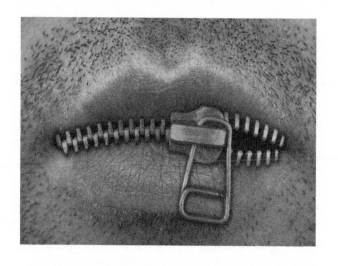

Carol was a 42-year-old mother of three who had known her lover Byron, a transport operator, for over twenty-two years. When Carol and Byron met, she was a struggling single mother trying to give her daughter, Stephie a good life. After Byron came into her life, Carol made many sacrifices to please him. Anything that made him uncomfortable or dissatisfied; anything he disapproved of; she gave up. She took a big risk by taking Stephie and going to shack up with Byron at his family house. Right from the get-go, his mother and brother made it obvious that she was not welcomed, but Byron's opinion was the only one she cared about – and *he* wanted her there. With him. So, Carol held her chin up and stayed. She prided herself on being a *real* woman - the kind of woman who put her man's happiness first, even at the cost of her independence and self-worth.

But living with the choices she made was not easy. Byron's family members did everything humanly possible to make her life a living hell. His brother Michael felt that Carol was the reason that Byron denied him access to financial aid and, as a result, she suffered physical and verbal abuse at his hands and lips. During one unforgettable altercation, amid the heated quarrel, Michael drew a shovel and only stopped short of hitting her with it when his cousin Kevin intervened.

Deep in her heart of hearts, Carol knew that they hated her because of her Indian ethnicity. She believed that it was this that caused the jealousy and hatred which led them to constantly stigmatize, browbeat, degrade and 'fight 'gainst' her.

One would ask why Byron stood by and allowed his love to endure such torture. But to his credit, Byron did in fact try to defend her. He had many arguments with his brother, who accused him of "putting dat likkle coolie gyal" over his own blood, but it was not only his brother that he had to contend with. Both his mother and Kevin sided with Michael against them. They told Byron that the only time he and Carol would be able to live in peace was when they packed up and vacated the premises. Through all of that, Byron remained steadfast and adamant that he would not leave since neither of the three owned the house and it was big enough to comfortably accommodate all of them. Why should he go and pay rent at "people place" when his grandmother had property that he could inherit?

So, where was Granma while all of this war and strife was going on?

Granma Matilda, being the sole, official owner of the house, was the only one who had the right to tell Byron to leave, but at the age of eighty-six, she had already suffered a massive stroke and had been bedridden and barely able to speak for years. While they were growing up, 'Granma Mattie' as she was affectionately called, had always told them that as long as the house was there and as long as the title rested in her name, they would always have a home. Byron took her promise to heart and told himself that this was where he and his family belonged and so he vowed never to allow his mother, brother and cousin to fight him out.

Every time Byron looked at Carol, he thanked God for sending such a strong, loyal, dedicated woman to stand by his side. Despite all the trials she had undergone throughout the years, Carol found it in her heart to look past the hurt, pain and unhappiness his kin caused her and managed to create a fairly decent life with him. For Carol, the sight of Byron walking through the door every evening and sitting down at the dining table to enjoy the hot dinner she prepared was always enough to turn her frown upside down. Their relationship withstood the storms and she ended up bearing two children at his request: a son, Khalil who was the spitting image of Byron – as everybody said; and a daughter, Janae who was 'daddy's little girl'.

Despite the struggles at home, Carol was determined to be the best wife and mother, and so she did her utmost best to create a happy home for her family. Although Byron was a good provider, sometimes the public transportation business was rough and so, Carol did her part to 'bring in the bread'. She constantly strived to find better-paying jobs, but when she realized that this was not enough, she contemplated starting a business of her own. She had gained several years' worth of experience whilst working as a Customer Relations Officer at a bookstore, and since she wanted to be able to make a positive impact, she decided that this was the industry she wanted to venture into. As a result, Carol became the proprietor of *Carol's Books & More*.

She had noted the direction in which the book industry was heading and followed suit so that she would be able to keep up with her competitors who had been household names for decades, thereby achieving sustainability. So, apart from the educational, leisure, religious books and stationery that she stocked her shelves with, she welcomed business from tech-savvy individuals by including an electronics counter where she stocked accessories for smartphones and other gadgets. The store also housed a cybercafé, a service she knew would appeal to the students at the nearby high school and college. The sign on the door read:

"Rushing and forgot to print your SBA or essay?
No worries.
Run-come get it done at Carol's Books & More!"

She did all this intending to build a successful enterprise. But even with the new business on her plate, Carol ensured that raising the kids and keeping Byron happy remained her top priority. As it turned out, Carol's Books & More enjoyed relative success, but sadly, over time it became unsustainable. Although the store was located in the vicinity of two institutions, its proximity to the other well-established, big-name businesses of the same nature accounted for a dip in customer-support.

Soon, she was struggling to make rent, least of all meet her loan repayment obligations in addition to covering the overheads. Ultimately, the best option became closing the doors of *Carol's Books & More* after only one year in operation.

Carol was beyond devastated. Not only was she left paying off a huge loan for a car which had played a vital role in the business, but she was also worried about looking like a failure in Byron's eyes. Even though he assured her that he was proud of her for giving it a valiant try, she just could not see it that way. Maybe she had been too focused on her desire to keep him happy... maybe it was just her wrestling with her insecurities about not becoming successful... or maybe it was the deep-seated fear that he might be thinking of a way out of the relationship that she had fought so hard to keep alive. She did not know where all her irrational thoughts were coming from, she only knew that losing the store caused her to lose confidence in herself as a woman and strengthened her doubts that she would never be good at anything. But regardless of the demons she battled, she still resolved to press on and fight harder than ever in her bid to bring about the success that she knew would please her beloved Byron. The bookstore perished and so did her doubts about other possibilities. She decided to pick up the pieces and move forward in faith. The entrepreneurial fire inside her refused to be doused. Shortly after selling most of the stock to her competitors, she invested the

proceeds in another venture. If she would have to stay at
home, then she would find a way to make money whilst
doing so. She did some brain-storming and soon
identified a need in the community that she would be able
to satisfy. This is how the idea for the daycare came
about.

Carol's Nursery built its clientele pretty quickly as there
were quite a few single women with young children in the
neighbourhood. The business thrived for a while, but
soon, it too became jeopardized. Miss Hyacinth–Byron's
mother, Mikey and Kevin soon began to accuse her of
'taking over the house'. They began threatening to wreak
havoc on her new business if she did not cease. And, true
to form, when Carol did not bow, they made good on
these threats. They would start playing music at high
volume and throwing words in a very boisterous manner,
especially when they knew that her young charges were
having their nap time. If the kids went outside or on the
veranda to play, they made a big deal about it. Miss
Hyacinth yelled and even hurled expletives at them and
sometimes the poor children were so frightened that they
would cry and run to Carol for refuge. After Carol
installed a swing set, slide and monkey bars in the
backyard, Kevin bought a rottweiler and let it loose so
that Carol and the poor toddlers became too scared to
venture into the area. Sometimes when the parents came
to pick up the babies, Mikey would pass very disparaging
remarks about Carol and the way the nursery was set up
within earshot of them.

Soon, more and more of the mothers stopped bringing their kids to Carol's crèche and she began to struggle with the prospect of another closure. She started to look into her life and question her choices. Why was it that Byron's family couldn't see how much she loved him and come to recognize the fact that everything she was doing was for him and the children who were flesh of their flesh and bone of their bone? What was it about her that made them hate her so much? Even after all those years?

And, what of Byron? It was his admiration and acceptance she craved more than any other's. What if she was never able to bring their family to that place of comfort and happiness that she always dreamed of? What if she continued to fail him forever and ever?

Sad to say, Hyacinth and her two minions succeeded in their mission to run her out of business. Carol stayed at home for a while and focused on mothering her own children after the daycare venture bombed. She found solace in the fact that she now had time and more opportunity to be at Byron's beck and call whether he was at work or home. She was always available whenever he needed her to please him in any way he saw fit, and she never heard him complain. If he did, it certainly wasn't in the presence of her or the children.

After a while, even though she thoroughly enjoyed playing housewife, Carol soon decided that it was once again time to seek employment. She had no desire to be one of those women who was content to sit at home while her man slaved to bring home the cabbage for her and their offspring. But alas, she was unable to see herself starting another business and so, the vow she had taken to be an employer instead of an employee had to be recanted. She had to try something else. Weeks of job-hunting left her discouraged and disheartened as she was unable to find anything lucrative. That was when a friend suggested that she try to "get a work a farin". Carol was the holder of a multiple-entry United States Visa that she had yet to travel on and so she thought about it and concluded that it would be a good idea. Though she didn't have a Work Permit and had no idea how to even go about obtaining one, she decided to reach out to some acquaintances who lived in the US to see what they could come up with.

She was excited about the prospects but was concerned about leaving the kids. Who would take care of them while she was away? Sure, Byron would be there, but they would need a maternal figure to nurture them. Even though Stephie was old enough to step in, Carol did not feel it would be fair to the teenage girl who had her own life to live and she didn't feel comfortable leaving them in her care, so she asked her cousin Jackie to be their guardian until she returned. Jackie and Carol had grown up together and were as close as sisters, so even though it would be hard to leave her children behind, she trusted they would be in good hands. She informed Byron of her plans, and even though he told her that he did believe it would work out, he still gave her his support and blessing.

She saw this as her final chance and a turnaround for herself and her family.

She hatched a plan to work for a minimum of six months, after which she would apply for a permit and travel at intervals to keep her job and simultaneously play an active role in her family. Shortly after making up her mind that this was indeed what she was going to do, Carol's prayers were answered and she found employment as a nanny for the children of a family of four. After much planning, an elated Carol packed her bags and said goodbye to Byron, the kids and Jackie just a few days later. She arrived in Fort Lauderdale and settled in with The Watson family very quickly. Although the salary was just enough to cover the responsibilities she had as a mother and partner, it was much more than she had been offered at the interviews she had attended back home in Jamaica, and it also helped to silence the voices in her head that had constantly berated her since the daycare debacle: *"You're a failure! You're a failure! You will never be a success! Give up! You're a failure!"*

So, she applied herself to her new job one hundred percent, with the thoughts of once more becoming a business owner and satisfaction at once again being a breadwinner for her family loitering in the recesses of her mind.

Even though she was 'working under the table', her employers promised that they would help to secure a permit for her at short notice. She was also promised time-off to see her family whenever she felt the need. Three months later, Mr. Watson told her that because of her dedication and commitment to taking such excellent care of his kids, she would be given a raise. Carol did not put much thought into it as the joy of being able to do more for her family took precedence. Besides, who was she to question good fortune?

Finally, everything was falling into place. She called Jackie with the good news about how well The Watsons were treating her. She, however, instructed Jackie to keep this hidden from Byron as she wanted to tell him herself.

Before she knew it, four months had passed and she was looking forward to seeing her family in two months. She was enjoying the time The Watson's took to make certain she knew how appreciative they were that she had left her family to come and take care of theirs. They did so in many significant ways: taking her out for lunch on the weekends or taking dinner home to her whenever she was not up to cooking.

Sometimes a "thank you" card signed by Mr. Watson alone would be left on her dresser. This made Carol wonder if his wife was not as appreciative of her services. Was she not doing enough to please the woman of the house? Nevertheless, she was grateful and was motivated to work even harder. She now considered herself a part of another family, but seeing their two children, Alex and Madison, made her miss her three heartbeats and yearn to return home to them.

The Silent Spouse

One Monday morning, Mr. Watson called in sick for work. Carol was surprised because he had shown no prior signs of illness. Mrs. Watson got ready and left the house sometime around eight o'clock, leaving the children to finish their breakfast and catch the school bus which was scheduled to arrive shortly. Mr. Watson slept throughout all this. At 8:30, Carol heard the school bus blowing outside which signalled that it was time for Alex and Madison to go. She escorted them out to the bus and gave each one a quick hug before handing them over to the driver. Carol stood on the pavement and waved until the yellow bus disappeared around the corner at the end of the street.

She then walked back into the house to start her day. She needed to do the laundry, clean the house, as well as run a few errands before the children and Mrs. Watson returned home. She started her daily routine by loading the washing machine while she thought about what to prepare for dinner. She wanted to get all of this done before going to pick up Mr. Watson's business suits from the cleaners. She was so focused on her tasks that she forgot that her boss was asleep in his bedroom.

"Carol!"

The faint sound of the voice calling out her name from upstairs reminded her that he was still there.

"Yes, Mr. Watson?" she answered.

"CAROL!" he yelled again, this time in a demanding tone.

"I'm coming, sir!" Carol raised her voice to make sure he heard her. "Be there in a second!"

Carol was not used to Mr. Watson calling out her name like that. She felt that it had to be urgent, so she sped up the stairs and walked briskly towards his room. "Mr. Watson?" she called out and knocked softly before opening the door. Carol did a double-take as she registered what her eyes were seeing.

She gasped and covered her face. *"MR. WATSON!"* Carol blurted, her heart suddenly racing. "Mr. Watson! What di hell! What is dis?"

For the first time since coming to Fort Lauderdale to work for this white family, Carol found herself having no other alternative than to remind him of her true Jamdung heritage.

"Missa Watson? A *mad* yuh a get mad? Weh yuh a call mi inna yuh room fah, an yuh know seh yuh nuh got on nuh clothes Sar? Mi nuh inna dem yah slackness ya, enuh! A only hope suppen really wrong wid yuh!"

"Ahhhh, Carol…nothing's wrong." The stark-naked Mr. Watson grinned seductively at her from his position stretched out on his side on the massive king size bed. "I've just been waiting for this moment from the very first time I saw you…"

"Which moment yuh talking bout, sar?"

"Carol, come on! You know exactly what I'm talking about. I see how you look at me. I see that look in your eyes and I know what it means. I understand, Carol. And I want you to know that I feel the same way." Carol gawked at Mr. Watson in disgust and disappointment. She could not believe what her ears were hearing.

"Which way dat, Missa Watson? Sick? Cause is soh me feel right now. Sick to mi stomach, sar! Imagine a *big* married man like you, ehhh? Sar, yuh really believe mi careless, ehh? Yuh tink mi leave all di way from Jamaica jus fi come lay miself careless, much less wid a married man? Mi did know, enuh –seh di whole a unnuh a di same ting. Listen to mi, sar – jus put mi money weh yuh owe mi togedda right now! An, as a matta a fact, yuh need fi pay mi fi di balance a di two month mi would a wok fi yuh, sar cause mi not stayin! If is a mistress yuh lookin, continue look cause me is NOT di one! Mi nuh inna weh yuh inna!"

As she stormed out of the room, Mr. Watson grabbed his robe, leapt off the bed and ran after her.

"Okay! *Okay!* Calm down, Carol! I am sorry," he slipped on the robe as he bounded down the stairs two at a time to catch up with her. "It was just a little misunderstanding. Please don't tell my wife," he sputtered.

Carol reached the bottom of the stairs and whipped around to face him. "*Meeee?* Tell *your* wife? No sah! A chuu mi nuh have nuh flight book mek your wife aguh come home come see mi this evening! Mi nuh have nuttin fi tell har seh!"

She knew Mr. Watson would comply with her demands, and because she wanted to honour her prior commitment to his family, she resumed her duties as if nothing out of the ordinary had taken place. The rest of the day passed without incident, and when evening came, Carol retired to her quarters.

While recounting that morning's event in her head and trying to fathom what had possessed her boss to make such an asinine move, her thoughts were interrupted by a knock on the door. Carol wondered if it was Mr. Watson so she did not respond.

"Carol?" said the female voice. "Are you sleeping?"

Carol exhaled with relief and hastened to open the door for Mrs. Watson. "Hey, Carol," Mrs. Watson had a look of concern written all over her face, "I hope I didn't wake you."

"No, ma'am," Carol replied.

Mrs. Watson rested a hand on her shoulder as she entered the room and led Carol over to the bed where she sat her down. "Mr. Watson just informed me that your daughter has taken ill, and you have no alternative but to return home."

Carol's reply was a knee-jerk reaction. "Fi mi daughter, ma'am?"

"Yes. My husband told me all about it." Mrs. Watson looked at her like she would a confused child or demented old woman.

That was when Carol caught on. Mr. Watson must have concocted a story about her having a family emergency back home to 'cover his tracks'. Since Mrs. Watson had come to know her as a well-spoken individual, Carol got back into character.

"Oh, yes, Mrs. Watson," she replied. "You have to excuse me. This thing has my head all messed up. My eldest daughter was admitted to the hospital last night and the doctors haven't been able to figure out what's wrong. She's not talking, not eating…not responding to anybody." Carol stopped talking and buried her face in her hands. She hated having to 'tell lie on sickness' as she believed it was bad luck to do so, but she knew it was in her best interest to play along.

Mrs. Watson patted her on the back in an attempt to soothe her. "Oh my!"

Carol shook her head and continued. "The doctors think it's a good idea for me to come home and see if seeing me sparks a change in her condition."

"So, when do you want to leave?" asked Mrs. Watson.

"As soon as possible, ma'am. I'm really sorry about this, ma'am. I never expected anything like this to happen," Carol told her.

"I know, Carol. I know. These things happen without warning and your family comes first. No need to apologize," the dark-haired, brown-eyed lady smiled reassuringly at her and Carol suddenly felt herself tearing up at the genuine empathy in her tone and expression. It was the first time that she was feeling so close to the other woman. "Don't worry about anything. I will book you on the first available flight out. Mr. Watson and I wish your daughter a speedy recovery and the best to you and the rest of your family. You will definitely be missed around here, but we will get by."

Carol nodded and accepted the surprising yet comforting hug from Mrs. Watson.

"You'll be in my prayers and rest assured that you will always have a job here whenever you're ready to come back."

Carol closed the door behind her boss' wife and leaned heavily against it. She was conflicted. The guilt of leaving Alex and Madison whom she had formed a strong bond with, suddenly weighed heavy on her. But she knew that she could not stay; not after what had happened. First off, she had lost all respect for Mr. Watson and after his actions; she knew she would never be able to trust him. Soon she would lose her love for the job and view it as an obligation. All things considered; she knew the best thing for her was to get the hell out of that house. *As fast as she could.* With that assurance, she soon drifted off to sleep.

She awoke the next morning to an envelope that had been pushed under her door. She tore it open like an excited child on Christmas morning and found a smaller one, bulging with its contents, inside.

As expected, she found cash. Her remunerations. As she had insisted. Doubled. And attached to this envelope was a note with two short sentences scrawled in what she recognized as Mr. Watson's handwriting: *"You are a remarkable woman. I am sorry about the way things worked out."*

Carol hissed, sucked her teeth and did not flinch as she ripped the paper to pieces. Disgust rose up in her stomach and chest like heartburn. The absolute gall of him!

She carefully placed the envelope in her packed suitcase and went off to commence her duties as per usual. This time, she made a concentrated effort to apply extra care to all her tasks since she would be departing the following afternoon, according to the itinerary and electronic ticket Mrs. Watson had presented to her before leaving for work. She felt a bitter-sweet mixture of happiness and pain as she led the kids out to the school bus and thought about the fact that soon she would be seeing off Kahlil and Janae again.

Departure Day finally came, and the taxi arrived to take her to the airport. Carol said her goodbyes with a lump like the size of Greater Portmore in her throat as she hugged the siblings, the wife and shook hands with the husband whom she decided not to "show bad face" in front of his family. Regardless of what he had done, she had no desire to destroy his life, even though deep down she knew he did not deserve what he had. The next thing Carol knew, she was on board Jet Blue flight 2975 headed back to Kingston, Jamaica.

Her arrival would be a complete surprise to her loved ones. She was worried about how she would tell Byron that she was once again jobless. After all, this was supposed to have been the brand-new start they needed. She glanced at her cell phone to make a mental note of the time. Forty-five minutes until touchdown. She looked at her home screen wallpaper; a photo of her, Byron, Stephie, Kahlil and Janae and suddenly the weight was lifted. The only thing that mattered was that she would be reunited with her heartbeats in a few short hours.

"Thank yuh, Jesus!" Carol exclaimed as the aircraft touched down on the runway at the Norman Manley International Airport and scattered applause erupted.

Once she exited Customs and walked out into the Arrivals Hall, she quickly reserved a JUTA taxi to take her home.

The driver took her luggage and led the way to where the vehicle was parked. "What's yuh destination beautiful?" he asked.

"Hughenden!" she exclaimed.

"Okay," he replied.

Even after the pep talk she had given herself on the plane, many conflicting thoughts fought to be heard inside her head as she sat in the back seat and stared out the window at the rolling landscape. What she most feared was how Byron would react to her showing up out of the blue, unannounced, nearly two months earlier than expected. Despite the rising anxiety, she knew deep down that he would understand, and stand by her decision as he had done on so many other occasions. This was comforting.

"Right here, driver!" Carol snapped out of her reverie and tapped the man on his shoulder as the car almost drove past her yard. "How much is it? Is only U.S. a have."

"That good, man," the driver assured her as he reversed and stopped in front of the black and white grille gate. "Even better, Fifty U.S. But since yuh soh pretty, yuh can gi mi forty-five and a smile and gwaan."

Carol laughed out loud as she fished the notes from her purse and handed them to him. "Unnuh man nuh easy at all! Blow the horn for mi please so they know somebody at the gate. I need my husband to come help mi with the luggage."

The driver took the money and then proceeded to comply with her request. "Looks like nuhbaddi nuh deh home," he said when nobody came out of the house.

Carol opened the door and stepped out of the car. "Everybody should be home and settled in by now," she told him. "Blow again!"

Just as she took two steps toward the gate, Jackie walked out onto the verandah.

"Somebody calling?" she squinted against the beam from the fluorescent bulb that illuminated the premises and peered at the figure standing outside the yard.

The driver exited the vehicle and walked around to the car trunk as Carol slid back the latch and opened the gate then greeted her cousin excitedly. "*Cuz!* Mi deh yah!"

CAROL!" Jackie exclaimed. "Girrrrrrrrl? Why yuh never tell wi seh yuh comin?"

"What! And spoil di surprise?" Carol laughed as the driver set the bags down next to her. "Tell Byron to come help with the bag dem!"

"*Byron!*" Jackie called out over her shoulder as she hastened to unlock the verandah grille. "Come look here!"

Byron, who was fixated on a football match, barely peeped around the doorjamb when he heard his name called then refocused on the flat screen television.

"Is who?" he asked in a gruff tone.

"Byron? Just lef di ediat match an come look nuh man!" Jackie told him as Carol signaled for her to be quiet and tiptoed up onto the veranda to crouch down at one side of the doorway.

Byron stretched noisily and got up from the couch.

"What happen, man?" he asked as he stepped down onto the veranda and almost jumped out of his flip flops as Carol launched her body into his unsuspecting arms. "What di –"

"*Byyyyyyyyy-RON!*" she shrieked as she held on tight and rocked him.

"C-Carol?" Byron stuttered as she kissed him all over his face.

"B-Babes? What yuh doin here?"

"A come home early, honey!" Carol explained as she held him at arm's length and looked up into the face she loved so much. "I missed you and the children so bad! Weh dem deh?" She craned her head around him to see into the house. "*STEPH? KAHLIL! NAAAAEEEEE?*"

"Sleeping!" Byron replied.

"But is just after eight. How dem gone sleep suh early pon a weekend night?" Carol was disappointed.

"Why yuh didn't tell mi that yuh coming down early?" Byron asked. "I would-a come meet yuh a Airport."

"I know you would, hon, but I wanted to surprise all of you."

Byron stared at Carol with uncertainty.

"What's wrong?" Carol asked.

"Nothing," he said, "Let me go and get your bags."

Carol believed his loss for words was an indication that something was amiss, but her focus was only on being home. As they all gathered in the living room, she fought the urge to wake the children by taking heed to Byron who convinced her to wait until morning. After Jackie retired for bed, Byron sought to find out the reason she was home so soon, and also took the opportunity to discuss other pressing matters with her.

Carol knew that telling Byron the real reason she had returned was unwise, and she felt embarrassed about the fact that a man she had left her family to go take care of had made a pass at her. Nevertheless, she knew Byron deserved an explanation. While Carol pondered what to say, her thoughts were interrupted.

"Carol? Mi get mi visa."

"Visa?" Carol was taken aback. Byron had not told her that he had been to the embassy.

"Yes, babes," Byron replied. "After mi see you apply and get through, mi decide fi try a thing to. But mi never tell yuh cause mi never waah talk too early."

Carol gazed searchingly at him for a few seconds before she took his hands and squeezed them. "But, Byron, this is great news, man!" she gushed. "I'm happy for yuh! Now we can make some moves together."

Byron looked at her as if he was terrified by what she had just suggested, and his response was a faint smile accompanied by a weak "yeah." But after so many years of being by his side, Carol knew him too well and this did not escape her. Instinctively, she knew there was something he was not telling her.

"What happen, Byron?" she asked. "Yuh don't seem excited for the future…"

Byron sighed deeply and untwined his hands. "Of course, mi excited…but is just that mi never know seh yuh coming home today and…" he paused and sighed again before rushing on, "It's jus' that a leaving tomorrow"

Carol knitted her brows in confusion. "Leave?"

She saw Byron brace himself visibly and wondered what was coming.

"Babes? Me a fly out tomorrow…"

"What!" Carol exploded. "Weh yuh seh? Yuh mean fi tell mi seh as mi come back yuh a leave? A wah dis? Yuh did a plan dis!"

"Calm down, C. My cousin send an invitation for me to come spend some time over there, man." Byron assured

23

her. "I am just going for two weeks. Mi tek vacation from work and jus' a goh cool out likkle bit. Is a simple ting man."

Carol cut her eyes at him and jumped up from the couch. "Soh yuh was just going to leave di children, without telling mi? Eh? Fi whole-a *two weeks*, Byron?"

"Carol... Baby... Jus' calm down. How long were you gone? Haven't I supported you every time you get up and jump goh do something in the spur of the moment?"

"Spur of the moment?" Carol echoed in disbelief. "Everything I have ever done, whether I was successful or not, I did with you and the children in mind. And, I always discuss my plans with you. Always. I'm not trying to steal your joy Byron, and I'm not upset that you got your visa, but you could have told me about this. What if I didn't come back early? When would I have heard about all of this leaving business? None of us would be here with the kids. Would that sit right with you?"

He took a few minutes to mull over her words before admitting that he should have dealt with the situation differently.

"I'm sorry," he said, as he stood up and went to her. "But the ticket buy already and mi bag pack and everything. Cho, man. Is only two weeks, baby. And I promise to call and text you every day."

Carol pouted like a two-year-old and melted into her common-law husband's comforting arms. "But mi *jus'* come back and mi was *dying* to spend time with you and di children…" she whined.

Byron cradled her head and dropped a kiss on top of the wavy, jet black tresses. "Mi know, hon. But is *just two weeks* and by the time yuh quint, I will be back," he assured her.

Carol lifted her head and Byron saw the tears pooling in her eyes. She was always so strong and determined that sometimes he forgot how emotional she could get. The sadness overpowered him as it dawned on him that he was hurting her. He kissed her Cupid's bow lips softly and she clung to him like she was afraid to let go. That one small kiss led the couple to their bedroom for an intense love-making session and as Carol surrendered to Byron's needs, she realized that he had not gotten around to asking her what caused her premature return. She was relieved that she did not have to lie to him.

***

Two weeks and five days later, Byron was still in New York. His return date had come and gone. He had broken his promise to call her every day, but Carol was not worried. She kept telling herself that Byron was just excited about being in a new country and place. She reasoned that his family members were probably taking him all over the place; doing all sorts of adventurous activities and he had even sent her a few pictures and videos to prove it. She was fully aware that there was a lot to see and do in New York City, and it was also on her bucket list of places to visit. Since she did not want to invade his space, she tried to maintain a cool head and keep in mind that he would be home shortly. After all, he had *promised*. And, if there was one thing that she could say about Byron, he usually kept his promises.

So, she made it her point of duty to find creative ways to occupy her time as she waited for him. Jackie had also decided to hang around a bit longer to keep her company. Jackie ran a beauty shop, so while the children were at school, Carol would go there to assist her in a bid to take her mind off Byron. She tried hard, but it was almost impossible for her to hide the fact that she was missing him like crazy.

"Look here, Miss! Di man soon come back! Soh stop mope around like smaddy dead!" Jackie would tease every time she caught Carol staring off into space or looking otherwise distracted.

But soon the two weeks and five days turned into one month. The one comforting thing was that Byron called to inform her that he had gotten an extension from work and that he would soon be back. But that 'soon' seemed to never come. One month turned into two and calls from him became fewer and, gradually, as two months stretched into three, communication ceased. He stopped acknowledging her texts on WhatsApp and one day she noticed that she could no longer see his display picture. All indications were that his number – the one he had for so many years – was no longer active. The pain of not seeing him or hearing his voice became unbearable. She managed to convince herself that when he finally returned, the fact that he had been away from her side for so long would be enough for him to never want to leave again.

But woman's intuition told her that something was terribly wrong. She knew that if she did not talk to him, she was going to go mad. Plus, Kahlil and Janae kept asking about their father. And, Stephie was growing more anxious with each passing day.

Finally, Carol was left with only one option. If Byron did not want to talk to her directly, maybe someone else could convince him to do so. She decided to turn to her in-laws. Remembering how Kevin had come to her defense that one time when Michael had tried to hit her with the shovel, she decided to reach out to him. She also knew that Byron's family were the only ones he cared enough about to never turn his back on, despite all they'd put him through.

She put aside her pride and poured her heart out to Kevin. For the first time in an encounter with any of Byron's family, Carol believed Kevin truly felt her pain and she was assured it was so when he told her he would do what he could to get through to Byron on her behalf.

Two days later, her phone rang. She knew immediately that it was her love calling. A lump formed in her throat instantly. Her lips quivered as she answered.

"Hello," she croaked.

Silence.

Carol cleared her throat and repeated the greeting. "Hello?"

"It's me," he finally said.

She could not hold back the tears that came along with the next words she managed to utter, "Byron? Please! Come home to wi!"

Byron realized the right thing to do was to give her some time to release all the tears and the hurt she was feeling as a result of his sudden disappearance, so he waited. When he thought she was finally through, he exhaled slowly and then whispered, "I am not coming back."

Before she could make sense of the very simple, blunt statement, Byron told her he had to go, and hung up without even asking about the kids. Carol clutched the Samsung Galaxy phone tightly for a while before it sunk in that he was no longer on the line. She knew that she had heard the words, but their meaning had not yet registered.

I am not coming back.

Carol felt her brow knit up as she stared at the blank screen that had now gone to sleep and replayed the five words in her head over and over.

I am not coming back.

She rose from the couch as if in a trance, tucked the phone into her bosom and walked towards the backyard where she knew she would find her cousin who had been helping her to do the laundry. She paused at the doorway and took a few deep breaths to compose herself before stepping outside.

Jackie looked up when she heard the approaching footsteps and the moment their four eyes locked, she knew right away that something was wrong.

"What happen?" Jackie dropped the piece of clothing she had been scrubbing back into the concrete washtub and rushed over to her.

Carol gripped Jackie's hands, and released a terrible scream.

"Oh God, cuz! A wah?" Jackie asked.

"Byron *lef* mi!"

"A *lie!*" Jackie gasped, but when she saw the look of absolute devastation in the other woman's eyes, she knew this was not a joke and she pulled Carol against her in a comforting embrace. "Lord have mercy!"

"Him not coming back, Jackie!" Carol dissolved into a quivering mass of bone, flesh, skin and hair in her cousin's arms. "Byron gone lef me and di pickney dem!"

Jackie held her up and took her back inside the house. As she wiped Carol's tears, she tried to assure her that Byron telling her that he was not returning did not mean he had *left* her or the children. She reminded Carol of the many talks she had held with him while she was away. She told her how Byron always talked about his desire to make a better life for her and their offspring.

But Carol was inconsolable. "I lived with this man for so many years. How come I didn't pick up that something had changed?" she questioned herself out loud.

"I understand that yuh in shock and confusion right now cuz, but think about it: did Byron actually *tell* yuh that is *leave* him leave yuh?"

"Wah else him could-a mean, ehh? A man tek up himself an' seh him a goh farin fi two weeks pon leave. An' while you an' yuh t'ree pickney deh ya a wait like Job, t'ree months pass and yuh naah hear nutten from him. Then him finally call and tell yuh seh him naah come back. Weh yuh would-a t'ink, Jackie? Put yuhself inna my shoes and tell mi wah you woulda believe!"

Jackie pondered Carol's incensed rant, trying to find proof that she was wrong and overreacting.

She suddenly got an idea. "All right. One way to prove seh him soon come back: mek wi call him workplace and see if wi can talk to him coworkers or better yet, him boss."

Amid the darkness, Carol saw a faint glimmer of light. She wiped her eyes and handed her cell phone to Jackie. Jackie took it and searched through the contacts for Byron's work number. "Just ask fi di boss – Missa Mason," she instructed. When the operator sent the call through, a gentleman answered after three rings.

"Alwyn Mason speaking," the voice said.

Jackie introduced herself and told him the reason she was calling.

"I'm calling to find out if Byron is still employed to the company," Jackie told him.

"Byron? Still employed? But I don't understand," Mr. Mason sounded confused. "When Byron tendered his resignation, he told me that he was migrating to New York. If you're his relative, how come you didn't know that? He gave me the impression that his family would follow suit. Are you trying to tell me that this is not the case?"

"No, it's not. But thank you for talking to me," Jackie replied. "I appreciate it."

She disconnected the call feeling completely bamboozled. She could not believe what she had just been told. Here was confirmation that Byron had indeed left the island for good. Here was confirmation that he had lied to her and had deserted Carol and the kids. What would Carol say and do when she told her that her suspicions had been justified? She could not look at Carol who had been hanging on to her every word as she talked to Mr. Mason and dipped her head as she rested the phone on the coffee table. Carol stared at her expectantly, waiting for her to tell her what she had found out. But Jackie kept her head down as she did not want Carol to see the truth in her eyes.

After several seconds that felt like eternity, Carol exhaled and sighed heavily. "He's not coming back, is he?" she asked.

"I'm sorry, cuz," Jackie replied. "Him boss seh him resign."

Carol was not prepared to receive this information. She stared straight ahead with emptiness in her eyes.

"Carol? Cuz? Seh something!" Jackie tried to get her to snap out of her reverie.

Every fibre of Carol's being was telling her to break down and bawl like someone had died, but she could not find the energy. She wanted to ask 'why' but deep down, she realized that she already knew the answer. All she could think of was the fact that she would never see Byron again, and for her, that meant the end of all her hopes and dreams. It was all over.

"Listen," said Jackie. "There must be an explanation for all of this. You deserve at least dat. Mek wi try get him pon WhatsApp."

"I think him block mi, Jackie."

"Yuh sure?"

Carol picked up her phone and brought up Byron's number in her WhatsApp chat list. She pointed out the grey "ghostie" that was there instead of a photograph.

"Butsiya!" Jackie exclaimed in anger. "How Byron fi do a ting like dat! Mek mi use my phone!"

But when she got her phone and checked, she was seeing the same grey silhouette avatar that meant Byron had also blocked her from communicating with him via that medium.

Subsequent checks revealed that he had blocked Carol from all his social media accounts. "Mi cyaah *believe* Byron could-a *really* wicked suh!" Jackie was livid and hurt for her cousin. As dedicated as Carol had been to him all those years, she knew he should not have done her so dirty. But it was for this reason that she felt something much deeper was going on. She felt a deep desire to get to the bottom of this mystery and help Carol get closure. So, she took it upon herself to conduct an investigation.

That night after Carol had gone to her room, Jackie took the laptop the kids used for their schoolwork and started her snooping. She soon discovered that Byron had neglected to block her on Facebook like he had done Carol and Stephie, but when she scrolled through his Timeline and photos, she didn't see anything unusual. He had never been one to post pictures of Carol and the children on his page and his excuse had always been that he did not want "frenemies faasing in his business." During her search, Jackie noted that neither profile nor cover photo had been changed. One was a random Google photo featuring the crest of his favourite English Premier League team and the other was of Byron leaning casually against the luxury Toyota Coaster bus he had been driving for Mr. Mason for the last five years.

But Jackie decided to dig further. If she had to end up in China to uncover the truth, so be it. She started combing through his Friends List for anything meaningful and it was during this search that she noticed that the profile picture of one individual was of a woman and a man whose stance was alarmingly similar to Byron's.

Alarm bells went off in Jackie's head and she immediately clicked on it so she could get a better look. Sure enough, it was Byron. Standing in the middle of what Jackie recognized as Fifth Avenue in New York

City. He had this woman that Jackie had never seen before locked in a very tight embrace and the two of them were grinning like the Cheshire cat and looking like two people who were very much in love.

Jackie felt the steam pouring out of her ears as she pored over the comments under the photograph and noticed that Byron's mother had typed: *"Good look mi son! Yuh finally find yuh perfect match!"* and Michael had commented: *"Yes, mi bredda! Shi carry yuh off! Yuh gone a lead now!"*

So, *they* knew! Jackie had to restrain herself from marching over to their side of the house and giving them a piece of her mind.

Still, Jackie felt that there was more to the jigsaw puzzle and she needed to find all the pieces to complete the picture. She now decided to scroll through the woman's profile photos and that was when she noticed that she had consistently tagged someone called 'Transporta B' in some of the most recent ones. Jackie decided to click on it and when Transporta B's profile and cover photographs filled the screen, Jackie almost had a heart attack.

"But a wah dis!" she exploded.

She could not believe her eyes.

"A wah a gwaan ya soh!" She could not control the flow of the angry words as they poured out of her mouth. *"No! No! No!..............*

She saw the light in Carol's room turn on and heard the door open.

"Is what happen, Jackie?" Carol asked groggily as she peered out.

Jackie was startled. She did not want her cousin to see this. Not now. Not like this.

"Is a show me a watch, cuz," she lied, as she hastily turned to position her body so that it blocked the monitor. "Sorry mi wake yuh up. Mi jus get excited. Gwaan back goh sleep."

As soon as the door closed and the light went off, Jackie refocused on the screen. No, she had not been seeing things. The pictures were still there staring back at her. And Jackie still could not believe her eyes. The profile photo featured Byron and the same woman from the first incriminating photo. Her Facebook Name was 'Mrs. Transporta'. In this one, Byron was standing outside a house with his arms wrapped around her hips while she leaned against him with her head twisted back to collect his kiss. *A French kiss*. Frozen in time for the whole world to see. The cover photo was the clincher. The one that had almost caused Jackie to blow a gasket…

A beaming Byron – Transporta B – was dressed in a black tuxedo with a crisp white shirt and a black bow tie and the woman – Mrs. Transporta (how original, Jackie smirked) – was again posing in front of him. She was dressed in a flowing white gown. Their left hands were interlocked across her bosom, the better to show off the sparkling diamond-studded bands that adorned each ring finger. But as if that was not enough, the picture had been placed in a frame of red roses with the caption: *To My Beloved Wife – Us Against the World 4EVR.*

The date stamp was less than two months earlier, which meant that the wedding had taken place one month after he departed Jamaica. There was the final piece of the puzzle. The picture was now screaming more than a thousand words at Jackie as she glared at the screen. Byron had walked out of his life with Carol and begun a new one – just like that.

But as Jackie took the time to scroll through the timeline photos, she saw evidence that Mrs. Transporta had visited Byron on the island – she calculated the trips in her head based on the postdates – one, two, three, *FOUR* times within the last year. There were numerous photographs of them at popular tourist destinations including Dunn's River Falls, Frenchman's Cove, what looked like Rick's Café and even one at Melrose Hill where he was feeding her a forkful of jerk pork from a Styrofoam plate. But the most telling post was a video of the two of them and a group of friends, including Miss Hyacinth, Michael and Kevin, enjoying a spread of seafood, festivals and Red Stripe beer at Hellshire Beach, which was dated just two weeks before Carol's return from Fort Lauderdale.

Jackie seethed as she took the time to save these photographs and even used her phone to make screenshots.

She put two and two together and deduced that Byron had met this woman – his now WIFE – while on the job. He drove a bus that often took people on tours to the resorts and attractions across the island. Clearly, somewhere along the way, they had gotten involved in a relationship which seemed to have taken off during Carol's absence. Byron must have seen this woman as the perfect meal ticket given that she was an American.

What an opportunist! Jackie thought as she logged out and shut down the computer.

It was a lot of information to process. Maybe this could even end up pushing Carol over the edge, but Jackie knew her cousin deserved the truth- the full undiluted truth. And more importantly, she needed to know *who* she was really living amongst. These people were clearly evil. She knew it would be best if Carol took the children and moved out. As soon as possible.

What a wicked set a people dem, ehh!

She shook her head over and over as she pictured their smiling, giggling faces at the Hellshire get-together. She felt the blood boiling inside her as she recalled the many glowing comments each one of them had typed under each of those photos with Byron and his new woman.

So, the next day when Stephie, Kahlil and Janae had all gone off to school, Jackie decided that it was time to share her findings with Carol. She knew there was nothing she could do or say to soften the blow, but before sitting her down to show her the evidence, Jackie hugged Carol as a means of assuring her that she would never be alone.

Carol experienced a rollercoaster of emotions as she looked at Byron's secret Facebook profile, the myriad of photographs featuring the man she had planned to spend her entire life with, gallivanting with another woman and she felt complete disappointment and the hot sting of betrayal as she read the comments that her in-laws had written on the wall.

When she was through, she just sat and stared blankly at the screen as the pain coursed through her veins. She did not want to cry. She did not want to get angry; not at Byron; not at his back-stabbing kin. But she had to ask questions.

"What is going to happen to the children? How mi aguh start over and rebuild wi life? Hmm?" She turned her puzzled expression onto her cousin. "What mi do wrong, Jackie? What did I not do? Is it that mi never pretty enough fi hold Byron? Or is it because mi nuh rich? Hmm?"

The questions gushed from her mouth like Niagara Falls.

Jackie tried to be the voice of reason. "Yuh didn't do anything wrong, Carol," she said. "And, yuh *tried* with Byron. Some people might even say, you tried *too hard*. To the point where yuh *bruk him bad*. And, you're beautiful!"

She rested a hand on her cousin's shoulders and shook her gently. "Cuz, you are a beautiful woman – inside and out. Loving, kind, giving, selfless… yuh know how many man out there would want to have a woman like you?" Jackie knew she would have to help Carol bounce back and she decided that she would not leave her cousin's side as she went through this trial.

In the weeks after she had learned the truth, Carol fell into a deep state of depression. She lost hope. Crying became her hobby. She was unable to perform her duties as a mother and Jackie and Stephie had to step in to take care of Kahlil and Janae's daily needs. Meanwhile, Byron was off in New York living his best life with his new wife. Almost every week, new photos were uploaded to the Facebook pages run by Transporta B and Mrs. Transporta, and Carol was unable to resist logging into Jackie's account (which he still had not blocked) to view them. Jackie believed this was intentional as he wanted Carol to see his posts and not be able to get over him.

Throughout all of this, Carol had not retaliated. She had not lashed out against the in-laws and had asked Jackie and Stephie (who was old enough to be told the true story of what had happened) not to either. She had refrained from trying to make further contact with Byron and had not followed Jackie's advice to send "Mrs. Transporta" malicious messages.

But, as Jackie watched her cousin pining away – not eating, barely sleeping, not leaving the house, not talking to anybody – she finally snapped and took matters into her own hands. She decided to inbox Byron on Facebook and, without making mention of Carol's emotional state, she told him that he would live to regret what he had done to his family, and vowed to find a way to make sure that he did not get out of "minding him pickney dem." She threatened to message his wife and let her know that she was a "man-tief" and a "home-wrecker" who "crosses was going to follow til the day she died." She reminded him about all the things that Carol had done for him since they had been together; how faithful she had been; all the sacrifices she had made for him. She sent him a few of the pictures they had taken as a family. She told him how Kahlil and Janae were asking for him every day. She told him just how disappointed she was in him, someone that she had respected and admired as a man who had been there standing in love with her cousin for so many years. She let him know, in no uncertain terms, how much he had let down every, single one of them by abandoning ship. And, she closed by stressing the fact that Carol deserved an explanation for his actions and demanded one on her behalf.

Jackie was surprised when his response came in the form of several voice notes a few minutes later.

"Listen," Byron said. "I would never leave my children wanting for anything. Mr. Mason has the money that is owed to me for all my years of service. I instructed him to pay it over to Carol and he is supposed to contact her in regards to that. Is enough money to tek care of Kahlil and Nae until I can start sending money for them. I would never abandon my children. I did this for *them*. But as for Carol, I left her cos I wasn't in love with her anymore.

And if shi really think about it, she will know is true. So, I meet somebody else and it just mek sense fi mek a life wid har. I took whole heap of time and ponder about this. Carol and I are over. I couldn't fake it anymore. So, I choose me. Is my time to be happy. That's why I leave. Please tell Carol to go and speak to Mr. Mason. Him will sort out di money business."

The final voice note came about three minutes later and it was the shortest one, as though it was an afterthought. "Jackie? Please let her know that mi sorry seh things end like this, and as soon as mi sort out miself, mi will link her to talk to di children. Tek care a yuhself."

Jackie was deeply moved by Byron's confession. It did not make her feel any better about the situation and, she wanted even more to curse him out and call him all sorts of names, but she knew that it was not her place to do so. It would change nothing. What was done was done. She also knew that Carol would not be able to handle this – hearing the alarming truth, straight out of the horse's mouth. So, she deleted her message and the voice notes before she told Carol about the money and that she should use it to make a fresh start.

After they had contacted Mr. Mason and found out that Byron had indeed made provisions for the children, Carol hugged Jackie tightly, and the flood gates opened once more. She cried harder and longer than she had in weeks as she finally accepted her destiny. Byron had ensured that the kids were provided for. She knew that this was his way of telling her that he would never come back.

He had left her.

And, she would have to pick up the pieces of her broken heart and move on. As she shed the last tear, and Jackie gently wiped her cheeks, she took a deep breath and let it out slowly. She was finally ready to let go.

Today would be the first day of the rest of her life. She was ready to let the healing start.

She squeezed Jackie's hands gratefully. "Thanks for being here, cuz."

Jackie had tears in her eyes, but she smiled weakly. "You're going to make it, Carol. You're a good woman. One man is not going to break yuh. Don't worry about anything. I will always be here for you and God have yuh back!"

******

Men. Where do you find yourself, if you are still searching? will your endless search result in a pile of slaughtered bodies left on the side of the road? If you kill the souls of your women then who will guide your children? What will be offered to them to help them find their place and purpose in life? Will the stories they are told by mommy be ones worth repeating? The stories they are told should be ones of love, peace and joy, not of pain, hurt and betrayal. When you take our hearts and souls, we become scared forever with regret and hatred for ourselves, wondering where we went wrong and if we were ever good enough. With your selfish actions, you take all that we would have to offer another, leaving only hearts that are broken. Because we were taken by surprise with the pain inflicted upon us, our girls are taught to always be prepared for the attack the opposite sex is expected to launch at them. We have no option but to teach them all the expected hit points, and all the angles that must be covered in order to terminate this destructive cycle.

Questions:

For the many females who have found themselves in a similar situation.

1. After giving her all to Byron, do you think there is anything that Carol could have done differently to keep Byron?

2. Is it fair to say; that in the end, Byron put his happiness and ambitions above Carol's desire to provide a happy home? If he did, was he selfish in doing so?

3. Should Carol have paved a way for herself and made more of her opportunities when she had the chance?

4. Was Carol too caught up in making Byron happy, and should she have invested her time into securing her happiness?

5. Did Carol's desire to keep Byron by her side become the ultimate thing that drove him away?

What   do   you   say?

2.

The Promiser

It is one thing for a man to neglect the vows he shares with his partner, but it is something completely different when his new interest is half his age, and she is in desperate need of finding someone who can allay her financial woes. In this case, anyone can be the victim. It is like a web that has been woven in wait of the right prey to be caught; with no subsequent escape for such… leaving death as the ultimate relief. This became the fate of one victim caught in a horrific game called love.

Captain was a fifty-year-old man, who was greatly known and respected in his community. A retired Police Officer, he got his nickname as a result of the advice and guidance he often gave to those who seemed to be in desperate need for such. He was the proud owner of a shipping company based overseas. His sons directed his company because they were living where it was situated. Captain never liked living anywhere other than his birthplace, but he still managed to play an active role in the success of his company.

His wife Catherine was a teacher who carried out her duties abroad because of a much better offer she received from the University of Pennsylvania. She too was nearing retirement, but knew it was very important to see her husband on a well-accepted basis; so she made sure she was home for all holidays, and if ever she could not make it, then he would take the trip to see her instead.

Thirty years of marriage and three well-grown children were enough for them to guarantee trust, honesty, comfort and passion to weather any adverse storm they would encounter. They worked hard to put their three children through University and made sure they assisted all of them to become successful. They had even bought a retirement home in a location they kept secret even from their children. It seems happiness was their only friend, so no one was prepared for any disappointment in this tightly knitted circle.

Captain was always ready to assist when needed; so when a colleague's community sponsored a project to refurbish a Primary school in his area, Captain was at the forefront and there was no issue getting as many hands as needed because he was a role model for many. He also made donations for some of the materials needed to refurbish the school. Captain did this with great pride and joy because he knew that this was where many of his associates attended school as children. On August 1st, one of Jamaica's major holidays, everyone was used to executing major projects or just dealing with unfinished chores at home.

This time around was a bit different. It seemed as if persons were just dedicating their day to what was taking place at the school. Everyone was set on giving their input in whatever way they could. Captain was on location directing and making certain everything went according to plan. After all, he has lived up to his name by being the front runner on any project.

Past students, parents, teachers, and community members were present; everyone was trying to get in on the action of making the school one that would be beautifully decorated and well equipped for the new term.

Even unemployed youngsters wanted to play a part, which they thought would make a good impression on their job résumé. One such young lady was Shari-Kay Reid —Shari, to her friends. She was a 5'4" well-spoken, well-shaped, long-haired young lady of dark complexion and slender built. At 18, she had just finished upper sixth form at her school and was successful in her examinations. She was now desperately seeking a job to put herself through university, as her parents made it clear they were not in the position to finance her studies. Shari was unwilling to let her dreams hang in the balance because of this impasse, so her only alternative was to get a job and do it herself.

So when she heard about this project that the school was putting on, she saw it as a great voluntary activity to include on her job resume, as well as a chance to meet new people. She believed the statement, "you never can tell what a stranger you meet might be able to do for you." And of course, her physique made it easy for any male to be willing to do just whatever it is she wanted; and that was exactly the case with Captain.

Shari and her friends Lacy and Calvin were busy at the side of the building applying paint to the bathroom doors when she caught the eyes of Captain, who was walking around the school compound making certain everyone was well-equipped for their tasks. He walked across to where she was working, and once he got close, he seemed to have forgotten his actual reason for being there. His eyes were fixated on Shari, and in that instant, every other aspect of his life came flashing before his eyes- his wife, his vows, his children, his home.

"And how are you young ladies and gentleman getting on?" Captain asked, making very sure to include all present.

"We're managing," replied Lacy.

"And you young lady? I can see that you are quite an artist." Captain said, admiring the designs Shari was creating on the bathroom wall, which gave it a completely upbeat look.

"Thank you, Sir," Shari replied.

"You are most welcome, my dear. And what is your name?" Captain asked politely, trying to hide the fact that he was smitten by her.

"It's Shari-Kay," she answered, "but you can call me Shari for short."

"Beautiful name," he said, "Alright Shari, it was very nice meeting you; all of you, and please keep up the good work."

With that, Captain walked away. But deep down he knew he could only walk away for that instance. His attraction to Shari was so strong that he questioned if he had done a good job of hiding it. The day passed productively, and all managed to complete the job they set out to do. After heartfelt thanks from the school board members, to all who had helped, it was time for Captain to give his expected speech. He expressed gratitude to all involved and how happy he was to see a community coming together. The crowd cheered and applauded loudly, and it was now clear to everyone that Captain played a vital role in the community. It was at that point that Shari realized the highly respected individual he was.

As the evening dawned, everyone said their goodbyes and headed their separate ways. Shari knew she needed to have a conversation with Captain before she missed out on a chance of ever doing so again, but he was already engaged in a conversation with one of the heads of the school board. He, however, glanced around to see if she was anywhere in sight. Her friends realized she was not about to leave, so they told her they were ready, as they all felt tired and needed to get home to rest. However, Shari's only intention was to speak to Captain, so she asked them to leave without her. Her friend Calvin took this as an insult.

"You mean to tell me we came here together, and suddenly you are telling us to leave without you? What's up with you Shari? You see a potential catch, don't you?" asked Calvin.

"What! Don't be stupid." Shari replied. "I just want to ask a few questions before I leave."

"Questions about what?" Lacy asked.

"That is none of your business now, is it Lacy?"

"You know what, Shari, you always seem to get your way, and something tells me this time will be no different. I hope for your sake whatever it is this time, it works out fa yah," said Lacy as she gave Shari a dirty stare.

Anyways, they left without her and with Calvin being the designated driver, Shari had no idea of how she would get home.

Nevertheless, her only concern was waiting for Captain to finish his conversation. And once he realized she was now all alone, he did just that. Captain hurried over to where she was standing, and she greeted him with the most breathtaking smile.

"Where are your friends?" Captain asked.

"They had to leave," Shari replied.

"And you don't?"

"Of course, I do, but I wanted to say goodbye before I did."

"Are you sure that is what you really want to say, young lady?"

"What do you mean?" she asked.

"Well, I believe the phrase 'hello' would suit this occasion."

Shari looked at Captain with admiration. They both laughed as if both smitten with each other's sense of humor.

"How will you get home?"

"Well, I assume I will have to walk, seeing that my ride left without me."

Shari said this with hopes that Captain would be kind enough to offer to take her home, and that is what he did.

"Don't be silly, young lady, I will not allow that. I will take you home. Where do you live?"

"Are you sure, sir? I would not want to put you out of your way."

"First of all, you can call me Captain, as everyone else does, and I am the one offering, aren't I? So no, you are not putting me out of my way. Just wait here and let me go get a few things."

"Ok," replied Shari.

As he walked off, she noticed a few persons staring at her which brought her a bit of discomfort. But she quickly reminded herself that she was used to getting stares by now, especially from females her age. She had always told herself the reason they stared was because they saw someone they desperately wanted to be like, so she smiled and waved to the onlookers as if taunting them.

"Are you ready?" Captain asked.

"Yes, let's go."

They pulled out of the schoolyard and, without hesitation Captain began trying to get to know all he could about Shari. She lived quite some distance from the school, so they had time to get to know each other. He did a very good job of proving he had the time for her by slowly cruising along the way.

"So young lady, it's the first I'm seeing you around here."

"Yes, apart from the distance, I don't go out a lot. Home is my place of safety and enjoyment, and I have come to love and appreciate that."

Captain knew right then that Shari was different from the other young ladies he had met because they always tried hard to get noticed. Without much effort, she had caught his attention.

"So how old are you, and what are you doing with yourself, Shari?"

If anyone else had asked her these questions, she would have felt uncomfortable, but for some reason, she had no problem whatsoever in giving this information to Captain. It was as if she was hoping these questions would all be asked.

"Well, I am the big eighteen," she answered. "Just finished upper six at high school, and I am now in a job frenzy, because I will be putting myself through University, and not going is not an option for me."

"Wow, you sound as if you already know what you want and have every intention of getting it."

With a deep stare and a slight smile, Shari answered, "Exactly."

For the rest of the way, they went back and forth in conversation. Captain found himself lost in her every word, without even realizing he had related parts of his life to her as well. He made sure he stressed the fact that his family was all living abroad and how lonely he was at times in an ever-empty house. She took the opportunity to make sure the empathy she felt showed, and Captain liked that. Realizing they were nearing her destination, and that she had come a far way to take part in the project, Captain asked, "How did you hear of the project?"

"My friend's mother is a teacher at the school."

"Oh, I see," Captain replied.

"Oh, you can leave me here, Sir."

"Ok, but why here?" asked Captain.

"I am fine here, Sir," replied Shari.

"I want to make sure you get home safely, my dear."

"As I said before, I am good here."

Captain carefully scoured the place whilst still making sure his expression gave Shari no clue that he thought the place was underdeveloped and unsuitable for someone like her. He thought the reason she wanted to be left at the roadside, was because she did not want him to see her true place of dwelling. He was worried about not seeing her to her gate, but he respected her wish and left her at her destination of choice.

"Well, thank you for the ride," she said.

"It was my pleasure, my dear, and thank you for your service to one of my communities. Let me know when the favor can be returned." Captain replied.

Shari laughed. Deep down she knew Captain would not come to her side of the world any time soon.

"Well, I must go. Will I be seeing you at any other projects?"

"If I hear about any," Shari replied.

"I would be delighted to let you know when any other comes up, but I would need your number to do that."

For both, this was a relief. They both knew they wanted to see each other again but, wondered how they would get around to that

"Definitely," Shari replied with a smile. She then asked Captain for his phone and carefully placed her number inside making sure there was no way he could lose it or even miswrite one digit. "Take care," she said, and with a smile, Captain drove away.

Captain was a man of class and swag, so for him, his choice of vehicle was a 2018 Audi. Anyone in Shari's community seeing a vehicle like that being driven in would be left with a lot of speculations.

As Captain's vehicle pulled away, Shari noticed that people nearby were chattering, and a few eyes were visible through the zinc fences that framed her community. However, having lived here for as long as she had, their actions were nothing new, so she just went on her way toward home.

"Girl, a so yuh a roll? Bap, bap!"

Shari did not even have to turn to see, as that voice was well-known to her by now. It was Lacy, the same friend that left without her.

"What! What do you mean?" said Shari with a grin on her face.

"Girl, dat deh fat Audi weh yuh jus come out a, a who a drive dat?"

"It's just a car, and just a gentleman that realized I had no ride home and offered to take me."

"Do you think I'm stupid Shari?" Lacy asked with a puzzled expression. "No gentleman not going to offer to take you here, just like that, I mean do you see where we live? Besides isn't that the same gentleman that was at the project, the one you stayed back to talk with."

"You know what, Lacy, you need to stay out of my business, and if you already knew who it was, why ask?" Shari responded with an annoyed tone.

"Sorry girl, jus memba mi did tell yuh. I really hope it goes your way." With these words, Shari turned, cut her eyes at Lacy and continued home.

Now Captain was home. All he wanted to do was sleep, but he knew if he were home all day he would have spoken to his family many times already, especially his wife Catherine, who checked up on him around the clock. When he finally got a chance to check his cell phone, he saw that he had missed many calls from her. Captain suspected that she wanted to make sure he was keeping up with his daily diet. He then tried returning her calls after showering, but to no avail. He had no intention of making her worry any further, so he left a message on her answering machine, assuring her that all was well with him.

The relaxing shower revived him; he no longer felt drowsy and wondered what could occupy his time for the rest of the night. He watched television, but that gave him no comfort. He wondered why he was unable to do anything to satisfy himself. The only answer he came up with was that he needed to talk to the person who had captivated him during the day—Shari.

He went numb as questions flooded his mind. He wanted to make the call, but would she pick up? If she did, would it seem inappropriate to be calling her at this hour of the night? All he knew about Shari was what she had told him, and he wondered if it were all true. He dreaded making the call, as he wondered if there would be a male's voice at the other end of the line. After all, she was of legal age to live her life the way she pleased. Besides, where she lived would be reason enough to seek help in any way she could. Captain hesitated, but then realized that there was no power strong enough to keep him from making that call.

He took up the phone twice before finally building up the courage to dial. He really hoped Shari would be the one to answer.

"Hello," a faint voice answered. Judging from her tone, he knew his call had awakened her from a nap.

"I am so sorry. If I had known you were asleep, I would have never called."

"No, it's ok," she replied, her tone now vibrant.

"I thought you would be asleep by now. After all, the workload was heavy today," Shari said.

"I have enough time on my hands during the day, so my nights may as well be occupied. Tell me, is it inappropriate to be calling you so late, or even so early?" asked Captain.

"It is never inappropriate for any call, as long as it is welcomed," she replied.

Captain knew then that Shari really welcomed his company. They talked for the rest of the night, with neither of them having to wake up early for work the next day, they lost track of time. Captain did not hold back in telling her how mesmerized he was by her beauty. She told him that she was attracted to his strong leadership skills, and she poured out her heart about the troubles she was facing in putting herself through college.

Captain was sympathetic, and for a moment thought of his daughter, who had a total opposite upbringing from that of Shari's. He and Catherine always made it their priority to ensure their children were well-provided for, even when they showed signs that they no longer needed that level of support. So, for him, anyone who never had that pleasure was worthy of his consideration.

By this, they both realized that they were engaged in conversation until 5 am, but for Captain, it was as if he still hadn't gotten enough of Shari's time; he was enjoying their talk.

"I see that I have kept you up," Captain jokingly said.

"Who's complaining?" she asked.

It seemed as though she always knew the right words to say to keep him intrigued and wanting more.

"Can I see you again, Shari?" he asked.

"Yes," she replied. "I most certainly want to continue this conversation."

"I am a lover of seafood. Can I come to pick you up tonight, so we can go out to eat and pick up where we left off?"

"I would most certainly like that," she replied.

"Where do I pick you up?" Captain asked, not forgetting what had happened the last time. He was given yet another location. He knew she was having an issue with where she lived and wanted to do nothing further to make her uncomfortable, so he didn't question the location he was given.

Ok. Will seven be good?"

"That's perfect," Shari said.

"Ok. I will see you later. Bye."

***

Shari's morning went a bit differently, as one would expect. Her idea of finding the perfect outfit meant trying on every piece of clothing she had in her dresser drawers; carefully matching and colour-scheming to get the right look for the right person. Her physique would perfectly fit into any garment of choice, but she wondered if her taste

was classy enough for a man as posh as Captain. She
opted for tight-fitted jeans, high heels and of course a
classy enough top to compliment it all, but soon realized
she could not find a top suitable for such occasion. In
frustration, she threw herself on the bed and screamed,
one that caused her mother to hastily rush to her room.

"Girl chile, is what?!" her mother exclaimed.

"Am sorry mom, I didn't mean to startle you."

She knew this was not the time to tell her mother about
the much older man who showed great interest in her. So,
she did what she promised she would never do to her
parents; she lied.

"I'm just excited because Mandy has informed me
about a new company that is opening and seeking
workers. She said that her aunt knows the manager and
would put in a good word for both of us."

Shari made sure she used a name that her mother would
be familiar with.

"Yuh mean Carly's daughter, Mandy?"

"Yes, mom, it's her," Shari replied.

"Good news that mi chile. Yuh si, that's why mi tell yuh
seh yuh fi neva give up. Mi know yuh aguh mek it mi
dawta," replied her mother.

She hugged Shari, and even though she felt bad about
lying to her mother, she somehow knew that when the
time came to tell her the truth, then it would all be worth
it.

"Oh, and mom, her Aunt invited me to a dinner tonight, and to maybe sleep over, just as a gift for doing well in my exams."

"Alright. Jus' be careful."

"You know I always am," Shari assured her.

Her mother did not hesitate to allow her to sleep at Mandy's home. Apart from the fact that Shari was an adult, she had also stayed with Mandy's mom on previous occasions.

"Ok. Just don't scare me like that again," her mom warned.

"I won't," Shari promised.

As her mother left the room, Shari once again became concerned.

"Oh my God! What am I going to do? I must look great tonight, but I'm not seeing anything in here to support that goal," Shari became hysterical! She suddenly remembered that her friend Lacy—the same one she told to stay out of her business—had recently received some luggage from her aunt abroad. Lacy told Shari that most of the items were clothes. For an instant, Shari felt a bit hesitant to ask a favor of that nature from Lacy, because she had always given the impression that she would stand on her own no matter the circumstances. She saw that she had no other alternative, besides, on more than one occasion, Lacy had also turned to her for help in finding the perfect outfit, even though the outfit came from Lacy's closet. She thought her advice would make up for her now borrowing a piece of garment.

61

Shari knew Lacy would not hesitate to help but no doubt would be curious, so she prepared herself for whatever questions Lacy would throw at her. Besides, the fact that she needed to look great tonight for Captain was more important than being tortured by her friend's inquisitiveness, so she made the call.

"Hey Lacy."

"Yeh girl. How comes yuh a call mi? Yuh nuh tink mi too nuff fi ansa di call?" Lacy enquired, proving once more she was not one to take anything lightly.

"So, I have this thing to attend tonight and I'm trying to find the perfect outfit, but my closet is a bit disappointing."

"Ting? Wat ting? Wah! Yuh a guh out mi fren! Is it clubbing? Is it like a private date? Where?! Tell mi! Tell mi!"

Shari was not surprised by Lacy's gush of questions. She had put up with that behavior for as long as she could remember.

"Look Lacy, where I'm going is not of importance. I just called because I am wondering if you have anything that will go well with tight jeans and heels. I have been searching from morning and not able to come up with a top that would work."

"Ha, ha, ha ha, woiiii. Where yuh searching?" Lacy laughed. "You know you did not need to waste such precious time. I can't recall seeing any piece of garment you own that would go well with tight jeans, let alone heels. But of course, you know I, on the other hand, am well equipped. You need to tell me exactly where you're going, so I can fit the outfit to the occasion."

"All you need to know is that I need an outfit for an elegant evening. Can you help me or not?" Shari snapped.

"Ok, girl, I see you trying to keep your date a secret from me. Must be top secret; anyways, come on over. I have your back, girl."

Shari wanted to remind Lacy of the more than one occasion she had to aid her in her attiring woes, but she once again recalled that Lacy was always the one with the products. So instead, she thanked Lacy and headed out. She knew time was of the essence; and the impression that she wanted to make on Captain was one that would require time and effort, as she needed to make a statement that would always be remembered. As soon as she got to Lacy's house, they started to hunt for that top that would enhance the outfit.

Lacy once more tried to get something out of Shari about the night's plan.

"All now, you can't tell me why you are in so much stress to look good... for whom?"

"Lacy, please! Just find the top!" Shari said.

"Isn't that what we're trying to do?" Lacy paused for a while. "Wait, this wouldn't have anything to do with that big man yuh meet at the school yesterday?"

"What? No!" Shari tried to compose herself. She was nowhere ready to let anyone know she was in fact meeting Captain.

Unfortunately, Lacy was one to read expressions very well and knowing her friend for so many years, it was easy for her to uncover what she fought so desperately to hide.

"Girl makes no sense you even try to deny it. Your actions give you away."

Shari could tell it was too late to try another rehearsed line.

"Ok. Yes, is him, but keep your mouth shut."

"I have been, because I knew it all along, girl. Make sure you know what you are doing. That man is much older than you—and isn't he married?"

"Yes, he is," Shari replied, "but he's living here alone."

"And that makes it right? A married man, Shari? I know you need the help girl, but this sounds like trouble."

"See, that there is exactly why I didn't want to tell you. I cannot take the judgment."

"I am your friend. I would be the last one to judge you. It's just that I do not believe any good can come from whatever this turns out to be."

"Ok, Lacy, I hear you, but please leave me to decide what can come from this. And please for heaven's sake do not mention this to a soul."

"Really, Shari? Mi look like mi luv chat people business?" Lacy looked at Shari in disappointment. And with that, she went in a suitcase, held up a top and said, "I think this would be perfect."

Shari jumped to her feet in excitement. She was looking at the ultimate winner, as she could see herself in that beautiful top, which somehow happened to carry the same shade of her chosen heels.

"Girl you knew you had this all along, so why didn't you tell me?" Shari asked.

"If I did, you would have left without telling me who your date was for tonight, wouldn't you?"

And with that, they looked at each other and giggled. Shari tried the top and it was indeed a great fit.

"Thank you, girl! I knew you would come through for me."

"Yep, always do, but will always tell you the truth, too, and the truth is, you need to be very careful."

"I will. I know what I am doing, and I know what I must do" replied Shari.

"Well, in the process, just make sure no one gets hurt," Lacy advised.

"Not my intention. Anyways, I must go. Please, please, please, remember what I said, not a word." Shari begged as she proceeded to leave.

"Ok." replied Lacy with a nod.

For Shari, everything was coming together nicely.

***

For Captain, it wasn't quite the same, because Catherine was expecting him to be at home later that evening when she called. He knew that would be impossible, so he made sure he informed her first that he would not be available to take her call. He knew he had to come up with an ideal reason and being married to her for so many years had proven that an explanation of that nature would not come easy, but he convinced himself that being graced with Shari's company was worth any explanation he would have to give. Nevertheless, Captain knew that when Catherine became suspicious of anything whatsoever—meaningful or not—she was not one to let go that easily. He believed that his best option was to keep everyone in the clear, so he made the call.

"Hello, hun, is everything OK?"

"Ok? Where were you yesterday, Mr. Smith?" Catherine asked.

Her tone was not the only indication that led Captain to believe that she was in a no-nonsense mood, calling him 'Mr. Smith' was not a common practice of hers.

"Honey, have you forgotten? I told you about the project coming up for the holiday. Well, yesterday was the holiday."

"It took all day for that?" asked Catherine. "And the time you returned my call, was just not acceptable. You know I worry when I don't hear from you. This is not like you—is something wrong?" she exclaimed.

"Wrong? What could be wrong? OK, I see something must be wrong for a husband to be thinking of his wife and calling to let her know. I was just caught up in the day's activities. I am sorry you were worried; guess you're really upset with me then." Captain tried his best at sounding apologetic.

"You know that's not what I mean," Catherine replied. "So, how was it? Was it progressive? Did you do all you set out to do?"

"Yes, and more," said Captain.

"That's great," replied Catherine.

"Well, hun, do you remember Mark Burchell? We called him 'Berchie' for short," asked Captain.

Of course, who can forget Berchie? After all, he helped you to be where you are today. He put in a good word for you, when you wanted so desperately to be a part of the force," replied Catherine.

"Yes, my dear; I can never forget. Anyway, he's here."

"Here where? Hasn't he retired now overseas?" asked Catherine.

"Yes, hun, but he's here for a short while. He came down to make some funeral arrangements for a family member."

"Oh dear, someone died. Please give him my condolences," said Catherine.

"I most definitely will. So later this evening I will be hanging with him, you know, reminding him of the places we used to hang back in the days."

"Oh, I see you two are going to have a party before the funeral," Catherine joked.

"Come on, Hun, you know I can never have any kind of party until you return home to me," Captain said, as he gave a guttural laugh.

At this point, Captain knew he was in the clear for his evening with Shari. His thoughts of enjoyment with her now became uncontrollable. He mustered up a huge laugh, almost as if he wanted his wife to know he had just gotten away with a barefaced lie.

"What's so funny?" Catherine asked.

"Oh, nothing Hun. Just had a flashback about the good old days with Burchie and me on the job."

"Hmm, sounds as if I should be there for this link-up later," Catherine joked.

"Don't be silly, Hun. It will be nothing; just talks about the good old days. Besides, it will be hard for me to have any fun when my mind will be fixated on you the whole time."

"My husband with the sweet words," she said. "Just be very careful and give me a call whenever you get back, even though I probably will not pick up."

"I will my dear. Love you."

"I love you honey," she replied.

Captain was now off the hook, but for an instant, he stopped to wonder why lying to his wife of thirty years had just become so easy. He took solace in the fact that this was not something done often, and that he was just going to sit and talk, something he felt she should feel no guilt in doing.

However, he knew he needed to get some rest for his much-anticipated meeting with his new-found crush. And being a man of swag, he did not need to browse through his closet for the perfect outfit, as it was arranged for all seasons and occasions. The only thing that was necessary at this point was sleep.

***

Time passed quickly, and Captain wanted to make sure Shari was still on board for the ever-anticipated meeting, so he opted to give her a call before going to pick her up.

"Hello" Shari answered.

"Hi. How's everything going?" asked Captain.

"Great. What about you?" replied Shari.

"Am here about to get ready. I think anxiety has now become my best friend." Captain divulged.

"Is it for seeing me, or merely for not being out in a while?" Shari joked.

"Who told you I've not been out in a while?" Captain jeered.

"Oh, sorry. Forgot you are quite the slick one." Laughter overtook them both, and in that instance, Captain realized he was finding himself in a place he had not visited for a long while—youthful exuberance.

"OK, I must go if I'm going to look great for tonight," said Shari.

"My dear, you do not need to do anything for that to happen."

"Aw, thank you," Shari replied. "I will definitely see you later."

"Before you go, are you sure you would not rather I come to pick you up at home. Wouldn't that be much easier for you?"

The temptation of saying "yes" weighed heavily on her lips, but her reason for saying "no" made more sense.

"I'm sure of it. Our initial place of meeting will be perfect."

"OK, my dear." Captain replied, and with that, he hung up.

Captain's outfit of choice was fitting. The fact that he took great care of himself and looked younger than his actual age did a lot to complement this.

He pulled straight blue jeans, a plaid long-sleeved cuffed blue shirt mixed with orange lines from his closet and complemented these with a brown leather belt and a pair of brown loafers, which were, by the way, the same shade as his belt. He complimented this with his watch and bracelet, which happened to be of matching links.

Captain knew he was a great dresser because of the many compliments he got whenever he got the chance of doing, so he knew there was no second-guessing his garment selection.

Captain made sure to splash on his favorite cologne, Million, which could be detected from even a mile away. He knew everything about him, had to make a statement, and that was his intention for this evening with Shari. With a huge smile, he got into his Audi and pulled out of his driveway. There was no turning back at this point, and he had no intention of doing so.

For him, there were no onlookers while driving through his scheme. His upscale place of residence was not one where persons got into each other's business, although at times that situation proved dangerous.

He arrived at the location where Shari asked him to meet her, and the huge open space gave him little hope of spotting her successfully, so he rang her phone.

"Hello," Shari answered.

"Where are you exactly?" Captain asked.

"I am in the coffee shop at the front," Shari replied. "But where are you parked? I'll come to you."

"Are you sure?" asked Captain.

"Yes." Shari replied.

"OK. I am right at the entrance of the mall. You already know my vehicle, so I'm sure you will be able to spot me."

"Ok, I'll be there."

Captain was so anxious. It was as if he was seeing her for the first time, and so he stared at everyone who came through the door. Suddenly his eyes, mind and heart froze when a beautiful figure came out.

Shari's hair was let down to flow freely. She was adorned in tight-fitted blue jeans and red high heels. She wore an elegant top which displayed her flat tummy, and a tattoo positioned below her navel. A red clutch purse to compliment her shoe and accessories, her flawless makeup and her gorgeous shape did everything to support her sense of beauty.

Captain stared at her walking towards his vehicle and all he could think about was how he had not seen a more attractive young lady in a long while. He averted his stare to not seem extremely smitten, but his efforts proved futile.

As she came closer to the vehicle, Captain hurriedly got out making sure he was available to escort her inside. It was now obvious that he was overwhelmed by the way she was looking.

"You look breathtaking, my dear," said Captain. However, Shari already knew this, because she had put the time and effort into getting it done.

"Thank you for your thoughts." She replied.

"Thoughts?" he echoed. "It is the truth. I am sure you must have trouble every day just leaving home."

"What about you?" she asked. "You are very attractive, I must admit. Besides, there will always be trouble, but it is up to one to decide if it's worth dealing with."

Her look when making that comment was one Captain knew very well, and he responded with a smile of approval.

"So, where are we going?" Shari asked.

"The way you look tonight, the correct answer would be, 'anywhere you want to go.' But because I have already made arrangements, you will just have to wait and see."

"I do not like surprises," she said, "but I guess I will just have to trust you on this one."

"Yes, you will."

Captain made sure he kept her engaged in interesting conversations. Her giggles echoed as he showcased his talent for telling jokes, and he was equally mesmerized by her laugh.

***

As they approached their destination, Shari realized that she was in an unfamiliar environment, because she couldn't recall ever seeing buildings of such architecture. She was a bit embarrassed to let him know of her unawareness, so she did her best to hide any trace of tension and anxiety. The vehicle pulled up in front of a beautiful establishment, and she could tell that this was a place frequently visited by the rich and famous.

They both exited the vehicle and were immediately greeted by the staff with welcoming demeanor who escorted them to their dining area.

Shari was captivated by what she saw. It was a setting for two with a soothing ambiance; the air was filled with the scent of fresh pinewood and lavender. She was surprised to find that this delightful aroma was coming from, which seem to be playing their part in the romantic setting for their evening. The all-white décor stood out, and it was complemented by wine-red table cloths, which were noticeably without wrinkles. Their table and chairs sat on white carpets sprinkled with red rose petals, which gave the room a beautiful, calming feel and look.

Standing at both sides of the table were waiters. Their uniforms were the same colors as the décor of the room. They assisted in pulling out seats for Shari and Captain. Both men were well-spoken. They wished the 'couple' a good evening, served them water and left to give them enough time to decide on their orders.

For a moment, it was difficult for Shari to decide whether she was in a restaurant or playing a role in a movie scene. But whatever it was, she knew this was something she needed to get used to.

"This is beautiful," she said, not realizing her thoughts were actual words. "I am sorry... did not really mean for that to come out."

"It's OK; it is beautiful," Captain echoed. "Are you ready to order?"

"Not yet. I just want to get used to this setting a bit more."

"Take all the time you need, my dear; there is no rush," he assured her.

They found themselves laughing and getting to know each other even more.

As time slipped by, Captain realized they hadn't ordered. Without asking Shari's preference, he summoned the waiter to take over a bottle of wine that he had requested on many occasions since going to his favorite spot, Champagne Brut Amour 2005.

Captain, being familiar with this, knew that it was most fitting for the occasion. Shari's choice of dish was Lobster in cream sauce with garlic bread on the side, and Captain being the polite individual he was, opted for the same.

She was not familiar with her choice of meal but wanted to make a good impression on him. So, whether she liked it or not, was not an option for her.

Throughout the night, Captain was greeted by a few of his acquaintances, who happened to be 'high rollers'. After greeting Captain, one of them took the time to mention how gorgeous she was looking.

Shari and Captain found everything to talk about, even things they conversed about before. She found herself once again telling him about her dreams, plans and how she had no idea of how she was going to get there.

"You do not seem like a young lady that will ever give up," Captain pressed.

"How can I? I will have to make my success. And I must get there regardless of the choices I will have to make to do so."

Captain knew right then and there, that he was without a doubt in love with the way she viewed life. "What if I offer to help you get there, if you promise me, we will get there together?"

"What do you mean?" She asked.

"It is very simple my dear, you need to go through your studies, but cannot afford to. I, on the other hand, can easily put you through your studies. I am not threatening you in any way whatsoever, nor will I ever hold the fact that I put you through school over your head. All I ask in return is that you genuinely be mine."

Shari sat in silence not shocked at what he said but, in an aim, to digest the fact that she had just been offered to be sent to University. She knew she would have to get a job, work hard and fight her way through, but she also knew that was easier said than done. And here she was being offered the opportunity to do so, and her only task was just to be with someone that she already found attractive.

Even though her answer was already yes, she could not let it seem as if she did not have concerns about the whole situation. She did not want Captain to think that the fact that she did not have concerns, made her any less of a woman.

"What do you mean *be your*s? Just like that? What about your wife? The last thing I would ever want to do is to break up a happy home."

"Nothing has to be broken up, and no one has to get hurt. I love my wife and my family, but I cannot ignore nor help the way I've come to feel about you. It is as if you complete me, and I won't lose you even before I have you."

Shari took a big sip from her glass of wine. It was as if she wanted to drink away her disbelief. She knew what Captain was saying was everything she had hoped to hear, but she never knew it would happen so soon.

The thoughts of her dreams becoming a reality, and the hope of a new beginning were the only force that drove her ego. She truly thought about the well-being of Captain's family, but the well-being of her life was far more important in that instance. And with her help sitting right in front of her, she wasn't about to risk losing him.

"Yes, I will be yours, but only if you promise me one thing."

"What's that?" Captain asked.

"We will take the chance and make it work, but as soon as the hurt that I'm worried about becomes too unbearable for any of us, one of us must walk away," said Shari.

Captain looked at her, as if puzzled. It is as if he could not believe he had met a young lady who was so much fun and so understandably mature at the same time.

"You are really one impressive soul," he said, "And of course, my answer is definitely yes. I would never want anyone involved in this to be hurt in any way whatsoever, but I will make sure that does not happen."

"Can we leave please?" Shari asked abruptly.

"Leave why? We haven't had dessert yet." Captain was a bit perplexed.

"I know that you haven't, and that is exactly why I want to leave."

He knew exactly the depths of her thoughts because he was no amateur to relationships

"Let's go," he said. He called over the waiter to get the bill, and he was no skimmer when it came to tipping his deserving attendants, and the waiter knew tonight would be no different, so he hurriedly came over to the table.

"Yes Sir."

"May I have my bill please?"

"Sure Sir." He carefully did his calculations and handed the bill to Captain.

"Thank you, young man. Here you go, and the change is yours."

"Thank you, Sir. Pleasure having you and the lady here. Please do come again," the waiter replied and bowed respectfully.

Captain's night so far had no disappointment, and he somehow knew the rest would be no different.

"Where to?" he asked, as they pulled out of their 'movie-setting' spot.

"I'm following your lead," she replied submissively.

"Tonight, you're coming home with me." Captain said. "I want to be with you tonight. Please note where I'm about to take you, do not think of it as my home. For the rest of the night, it is our home."

***

As she allowed Captain to take her to his home, she began recalling her parents lashing out at people who defiled their marital bed, and how the Lord would deal with them.

"Will I also be punished?" she thought to herself. "Will I be the reason Captain defiles his home? If so, how will I be punished?"

"I can't do this. I mean, I want to, but just not there." Shari eventually blurted.

"It is OK my dear. I know that you are a woman of conscience and class, so I know you are more concerned with my vows, rather than what will make you happy. I can assure you, no law within my home will be broken tonight, and no one will get hurt. I need your presence there tonight."

Captain's soft tone and warm touch meant more to her than her guilty conscience. And with those convincing words she conceded, "Ok, I will go with you."

"We are close by anyways." Captain smiled.

She now realized that she was in his territory, as the beauty of the place had started to dawn on her sight. It was much different from her usual surroundings.

"Wow! This is where you live?"

"Yes, this is it."

Captain pulled up to a high-rise setting, its gate opening at the command of his voice. When he drove in, the house was at a distance beyond the gate, so there was a lot to view before the house itself.

Shari noticed that trees were forming a perfect sculpture of adjoining arches. She held her head low as Captain drove under as if she was trying to get a view of the house, even before arriving there. She tried to keep her composure knowing she had only seen settings of this nature in the movies.

"Don't worry," he assured her. "You can also make all this happen. Just be true to me."

In that instant, she knew the help she desperately needed was finally here.

Shari saw a huge white building straight ahead; she thought she was at the Governor General's house. The doors and windows were all glass and a beautiful lawn with lights encircled the house. Captain got out and opened her side of the car.

"Welcome to my Palace," he said, as he ushered out the car.

As Shari walked towards the door, she had flashes of discussions she had with her friends about what they would like their life to be like. This is where she needed to get, and for her, Captain was the only one who could get her there.

He disarmed the alarm system guarding his palace and entered with Shari close behind him. As he flicked the light switch, Shari was in even more awe.

"Are you ok, Boo?" Captain asked.

"Sure, I'm fine. It's just that I have never seen such beauty at its finest."

Captain laughed. "My dear, this is nothing compared to some of my close associates' houses. My circle has always been filled with people who strived for excellence."

As he spoke, she noticed that his eyes were busy glancing across her well-toned body.

"Make yourself comfortable," he said. "My home is yours. Would you like something to drink?"

"Some water would be fine."

"Water? Are you sure?"

"Yes, remember we are just getting back from dinner."

"That's true, my dear, but you are with me now. You are safe; you can have whatever you like."

He opened his well-designed liquor cabinet and told her to choose a wine of her choice. Not familiar with the variety on display, she simply chose one that had a colorful appearance.

"Great choice," Captain said, as he poured her glass and handed it to her. He rolled out an extended bed hidden in the form of a sofa. He then asked her to sit and relax before kneeling to remove her shoes. She shied away a bit but remembered how he said she was safe with him. Captain then turned on the soothing sound of Marvin Gaye's, 'Let's Get It On' in an attempt to create a romantic ambience.

"Shouldn't you check in with your wife?" Shari asked.

"My wife knows my schedule. We do not need to check up on each other. Besides, why ask about my wife? We are here now." Captain knew Catherine was expecting his call regardless of what time he got in, but he decided at that moment, that what he had, was far more important than any anger his wife would hurl at him for not calling.

Shari's thoughts were interrupted by the ringing of her cell phone. She saw that it was her mother calling to check in on her. By now the wine was getting to her head, and even though she dreaded talking to her mom, she knew she must take the call as her mother was always one to worry. She asked Captain to lower the music a bit.

"Hi, mom."

"Yuh ok, mi dawta?"

"Yes. Mandy and I are just lying down and planning how we will approach everything."

"That's good. Yuh really have yuh head together. Jus mek mi tell har mada goodnight."

"Mom, she's already in bed."

"Oh, alright den, jus waan know yuh safe, but how yuh sound suh?"

"How do I sound, mom?"

"Yuh vice kina sound different. Yuh sure yuh alright?"

Shari realized the wine was playing with her head, so she fought hard to maintain her composure.

"Am good, mom," said Shari. "We are just full and tired, that's all."

"Ok, tell Mandy good night fi mi, and be careful. Try to come home early tomorrow."

"I will, mom, and goodnight."

Shari dropped her head low, this time not because of the wine, but because she believed being dishonest with her mother was now becoming a pattern.

"Is everything alright?" Captain asked as he increased the volume on the music now that Shari had finished talking to her mother.

"I just lied to my mother again," Shari whispered.

"Why?"

"Excuse me! Was I to let her know I was spending the night with a married man?" she glared at him.

"Of course not, boo. Don't tell her where you are but do it truthfully. Tell her you are spending the night with a friend. Now isn't that the truth?"

Shari stared at Captain in a daze. Was she with someone who played this part before?

"My mother is not like others. She actually worries about me."

"Who wouldn't? Look on the bright side. Your mother is assured that you are perfectly safe. That is what matters."

Shari smiled, now she felt a bit better.

"Would you like to watch a movie?" he asked.

"I don't see why not."

"What's your choice?" he asked.

"Why don't you choose? You have been doing great so far?" she replied.

"OK, my dear, let the theme be romance since I am feeling very romantic tonight."

As he pulled open the door of the cabinet that housed the television, Shari realized once again her expectations were met.

"Are we actually at the cinema?" she jeered.

Captain laughed. He knew she was referring to the enormous size of the television set. "This is a small one," he said

"If you are a giant." She replied.

She was thrilled to find that his choice of movie was '50 Shades of Grey', one of her favorites.

"Your taste in everything just gets better and better," she said. She shifted herself a bit, giving him an invitation to lay next to her. He was now half-dressed, wearing only sweatpants.

"Are you OK, boo?"

Shari felt chills running through her body, as the firmness of Captain's bare chest pressed against her back.

"Why are you breathing so hard, boo?" he asked. "Relax, you are safe."

His hands brushed her hair away from her face and tucked it behind her ears.

"I want to see your beautiful face," he said as he gently nudged her onto her back.

Shari knew what she wanted to say but the words were not forthcoming.

Captain then pressed his lips over hers, and with a firm soft voice, he said, "Tonight we become one."

It was her first experience of intense sexual passion. No matter how much she wanted to resist what was happening, it was beyond her capabilities. In that moment, the only thing that mattered and felt right was the pleasure of flesh. Captain seemed to sense her aura, and for that night, his only aim was to please her. Her warm tears streaked down his huge shoulders as he lifted her head and gently kissed her lips.

"I know these are tears of pleasure," he softly said. "I will continue making you happy."

Shari knew there was no turning back and she had no intention of putting this feeling to an end. She experienced pleasure repeatedly. She never thought it would be possible with someone more than twice her age; she began wondering if she was in love, and that thought gave her comfort as she laid.

…

It was now morning, and Shari woke up to the soft kiss of Captain's lips.

"Good morning love. How was your night?"

"I stayed, I slept, I…." Shari paused, aware of what had taken place, but opted not to speak of it.

"My darling, I tasted every bit of your body," Captain reminded her, "It was unbelievably sweet."

Shari held her hair up as she heard his full recap of their night.

"I need to get home," she said.

"It's only five. Can't you stay for another hour?"

She wanted to but she decided that declining would be the most appropriate thing to do, as she knew staying would take her once more into his arms.

"I must go, but I enjoyed the time spent."

"OK. Let me get dressed, and I'll take you."

"No!" she exclaimed. "Can you just call me a taxi, please?"

The same vehicle taking her home, pulling up to her side of the world in the wee hours of the morning, would eliminate any doubts about where she had been all night. Captain realized she was uncomfortable with him taking her home, so he recanted his words.

"Ok, but at least have some orange juice," he said.

"Thank you, I will."

As she waited for the taxi to arrive, h Captain poured her a glass of orange juice. Studying her face, he could tell that she was a bit confused, and he would never in a million years want her thoughts to become regrets.

"Are you OK?" he asked again.

"Yes, I am fine," she replied as she sipped her orange juice.

Captain knelt in front of her, took her hand in his, looked her straight in the eyes, and told her she had nothing to worry about. He told her that after last night, she had become a part of his whole being.

Shari smiled. She felt assured.

"Thank you," he said, "I have not felt like this in years. You reminded me of how it feels to be wanted, and I will never forget that. I will always be there for you; you can count on me."

His words were interrupted by a tooting horn; the taxi was outside, so it was time to pull away from Captain.

"Can I give you some money, boo?

"OK," she hurriedly replied.

Captain reached for his wallet and took out some bills.

Shari knew that attempting to count how much it was in front of him was bad manners, so she placed it inside her bag.

"Thank you."

"No worries, boo. I will call you later when you are settled."

He disarmed the alarm and took her to her ride. As he instructed the driver to see her safely home, he gave a salute to a fellow neighbour driving by. Shari noticed that they both exchanged a wink. She thought this strange but last night's pleasure blocked any thought of something being amiss.

As the taxi carried her off, she felt a sudden rush of regret about lying to her mother, even though sleeping away from home was not something she did regularly. As the taxi turned towards her lane, the unfinished and unpainted buildings gave her a heads-up that she was close to home. Some neighbours had risen earlier than usual; it was a Saturday morning, and the fact that there were not many employed individuals living in her community had contributed to the phrase, 'Late to bed, early to rise' being associated with her community.

"Miss, where a mus leave yuh?"

"Can you please pull up to the top of the lane?" Shari replied.

"But mam dis a lane. If a go up in there, how mi aguh reverse? Yuh know wat? Is OK. Mi wi dweet, cuz di big man se mi fi mek sure yuh get home safe, an mi work fi him already, and mi rispek seh him use mi back."

Shari sighed with relief. She was in no way, shape or form prepared for the many stares, whispers or questions that would be thrown her way. As the taxi passed Lacy's house, she realized Lacy was not up as yet. Shari knew she must still be prepared to deal with questions later.

"Thank you, Sir. How much is it?"

"Yuh gud man sweet girl, the big man tek care a it aredi. Jus mek him know yuh reach gud."

"Ok, I will. Thanks again."

As she slammed the car door shut, and the taxi pulled away, Shari's mom came outside to see who it was.

"Wait, yuh really come home early."

"I have things to do today, mom, so I want to get an early start."

"Today is Saturday enuh chile. But anyways yuh always working, suh is alrite. Everything guh ok?"

"Of course," Shari said, as she headed toward the drawn curtain that separated her room from the passageway.

"Wait, yuh not going to tell your fada gud mawnin?"

"Is who dat? Shari?" her father questioned.

"Yes, dad." She crossed the passage and peeped inside to see him still lying in bed watching the television.

"Young lady yuh home, hmmmn... turn big woman now?"

"No, dad, I just stayed by a friend."

"Is trouble a troubling yuh. Yuh mada told mi. Glad fi si yuh home gud."

"Yes, dad, I will talk with you later. I am going to lie down."

"Lie down? Is how unno young people love lie dung suh? Yuh nuh si sun come up?"

"Dad, I am very tired," she muttered.

"Hmmmn! Alright mi chile, get yuh rest."

Shari went to her room and pulled the curtain to hide her exhaustion. After last night, she was confused as to whether or not she wanted to forget it all or place it in her hidden memories never to be erased. Her mixed feelings were too much for her, and she fell asleep.

***

Well, for Captain, he knew he had once more failed to let his wife know he had gotten home safely. He always managed to get her to believe his tales of how he spent his days. The explanation leading up to that was always a burden, but the night spent with Shari was enough to ease this. It was still early enough to give Catherine a call without raising too much suspicion. He was about to do so when suddenly the phone rang.

"Lord, please don't let this be her." He prayed audibly.

He stared at the phone to see if the number would be one he did not recognize, but his hope was quickly shattered.

"Good morning, my sweetheart. They say great minds think alike, as I was just about to call you."

"Really now? I thought you were supposed to call me last night."

"No Hun, I told you I would call you when I got home, and no, I am not just getting home, but when I did it was very late. You know I hate disturbing you late at night."

"Disturb! You are my husband, and that should be one of your main jobs. You seem to be very caught up lately. What's going on? Is everything OK?"

"Of course, everything is OK, And what do you mean 'caught up'? I have only missed calling you a few times, and besides, you know what last night was about. Burchie and I really caught up on lost times. We went out for a few beers and even invited a few more of the crew. We lost track of time, trust me."

"I know, Hun, and it is OK, but I also know something about you seems different. You seem a bit happier, so I will not complain," said Catherine.

"If I sound happy it is because I am hearing your voice," Captain replied. He knew his true source of joy was connected to the fact that Shari had walked into his life, but he also knew he loved his wife and would do everything in his power to keep her from getting hurt.

"My husband with the sweet words," Catherine said. Well, it's my turn to give you some sweet words now."

"What, you love me more?" Captain smirked.

"You know I do, but even better. The school has this program where they are taking on practice teachers just out of college; part of giving them support and preparing them for the world of teaching. Well, they have asked a few of us Senior Teachers to assist by allowing them to take our place in the classroom—along with their mentors—to get familiar with areas of their major and an understanding of how the school system operates."

"You mean like a wife swap?" Captain jeered.

"Ha, yes, but instead, teachers will be the ones making the swap. Anyway, I am one of the volunteers, and I was quick in doing so because not only will I get a long-overdue break, but I will still collect my salary for my time of absence. Those three months will be like a lifetime of rest."

"Three months? That's the duration?"

"Yes, I leave two weeks from today."

There was silence on the other end. "Hello," Catherine said.

Captain finally responded, "I am here. I just don't know how to show how happy I am. I wasn't expecting you until summer, and now you will be right with me in March."

"I know, hun!" Catherine shrieked. "I would never miss out on this opportunity. I miss you so much."

"I miss you too, more than you could ever imagine," Captain replied. "So, have you told the children as yet?" he asked.

"No. Not yet. They are very busy with the business and their lives, but I will let them know."

"Ok. So, I have my wife home in two weeks. It's long overdue."

"I know, and I will make it up to you."

"OK, my love. I am late and will definitely talk to you later."

The news of Catherine coming home had left Captain with mixed thoughts. He truly missed her and wanted her by his side, but he could not shut out the feelings he had developed for Shari, and not spending another night like the one he had with her would be unbearable. The "what ifs" danced across his mind as he wondered how he would handle this unexpected situation.

There was no room for mistakes or repercussions, ones he knew would now find their place in his life, a life he had fought so hard to build. He had to make sure there would be no surprises for anyone involved, especially his dear Catherine. He thought the only way to prevent this from happening was to make Shari aware of what would take place in two weeks to come.

Captain knew Shari would be tired from last night, so he wanted to wait until the afternoon to update her.

It was now midday, and Captain felt that was enough time for her to be rested. He rang her phone four times but to no avail. Maybe she was more tired after last night than he had expected. With a prideful grin, he opted to get some rest himself. Halfway to his bedroom, the phone rang. It was Shari, returning his call.

"How are you?" Captain asked.

"A bit tired, but well otherwise." She left out the part where she was having mixed thoughts about the events of her pleasurable night. She wouldn't want Captain to feel he was the reason.

"Expected, my dear," Captain replied. "Let me first say again that I had a splendid night, and I have no regrets. I only hope it will repeat itself."

Shari quietly uttered, "I feel the same."

"Anyways my dear, I called because there will be a change for the next two weeks and I wanted to be the one to let you know."

"Change? What do you mean?"

"My wife is coming."

"Coming? Coming where?"

"Coming home" Captain repeated.

Shari knew what she heard but thought she was probably still half-asleep, and this was just one of the unwanted voices in her miserable dream.

"What do you mean coming home? When?"

"Two weeks from today," he answered.

"Did you know this before you slept with me?"

She quickly realized the words that came from her mouth and composed herself, worried that her parents would hear her outburst.

"Please don't sound like that," he pleaded. "I did not know. She only told me this morning. I know it's sudden, and I was not prepared for this either, at least not so soon. But boo, we have two weeks to find out more about each other, and after she leaves, you can have me all to yourself again."

"Two weeks? And then what happens when she's here? I sit and count the days like some unwanted puppy until she leaves?"

"Actually, It's months." Captain replied

"What!" Shari could not contain her shock.

"She'll be here for three months."

Shari went silent. Her friend Lacy's words suddenly came back to her, and her promise to herself of not being just a side chick suddenly became a regretted reality. She could not hold back the tears.

"I knew this would happen," she said. "I expected it, but now that it's here, I feel cheated and used."

"What are you talking about, boo? No one used you. Remember my home is also that of my wife's, and she is free to come and go as she pleases. You act as if I planned this. You are taking all this out of context. I still want to be with you. My wife coming home changes nothing. Any promise I made to you will not be broken. Not by me."

Shari tried to find comfort in Captain's desperate assurances, but the hurt and betrayal she felt carried much greater weight. She was now sure, she was in love with Captain, and it hurt.

"I can't do this. I know it's not your fault but coming to see you before your wife arrives is not an option for me right now. Goodbye Captain."

Shari hung up the phone.

It rang again—and again—and again, but she ignored it because she wanted to be left alone; at least for now.

She had to leave home at least for the moment because she could do nothing to stop the uncontrollable tears. Her parents were good people, and she would never forgive herself if they found out that she had disappointed them in such a manner. With tears flowing down her face, she went to the only person she knew would comfort her, but also tell her the truth at the same time. Ignoring all onlookers, she cried her way down the busy lane towards Lacy's house.

"Wait, a nuh Ms. Madge dawta dat?" said an old lady sitting outside her gate. "Wait? A weh di crocodile tears fah? A how unnuh young people cya bawl suh nowadays? Unnuh have too much trouble man cho."

Shari ignored the woman. Her only aim was to get to Lacy's house, even though she knew Lacy would give her the "I told you so" lecture.

"Lacy!" Shari called out as she opened the gate and headed toward the door.

"Shari is that you? Why are you crying?" Lacy asked.

Shari rushed into Lacy's room and threw herself on the bed, allowing the tears to flow even more.

For Lacy, seeing her friend in distress was heartbreaking.

"Tell me what's wrong," Lacy demanded.

"I'm so ashamed. You were right. You warned me about getting hurt." Shari replied.

"What are you talking about?"

"Please don't be mad at me, and most of all, don't judge me."

"I never judge you. I tell you the truth, but I have never judged."

"I slept with him, Lacy." Tears overtook her voice until she repeated, "I slept with him. I did, and he's married."

"Who's married? Who did you sleep with?"

Lacy recalled her prior conversation with Shari, when she desperately wanted an elegant look.

"Wait... Are you talking about that man you met at the project?" Lacy asked.

Shari glanced up at Lacy's piercing stare and then embedded her face in the pillow. That was the only confirmation Lacy needed.

"Shari, you didn't! He's married. But why are you crying like this?"

"Because he called me to tell me his wife is coming in two weeks."

"I knew no good could come from this. I warned you." Lacy stopped cussing, likely realizing the 'blame game' was the last thing Shari needed.

"Look girl, don't beat up on yourself so much," she went on. "You are young, you are human, and you make mistakes, maybe even more to come. Besides, it's his fault. He's the one married." said Lacy.

"But I knew that he was, and I still slept with him."

Lacy finally realized the nature of Shari's damning mistake.

"Do your parents know?" she asked.

"Are you crazy? And they can never know."

"Not by me, girl, count on that. So, what is he saying now?"

"He wants me to spend two weeks with him before his wife comes."

Lacy blinked. "I hope you are not even considering that. You have messed up. Get past that and move on. No permanent damage has been done. Forget him and get back on track with plans for your future."

"He is a part of them."

"Excuse me, Shari! Who is a part of them?" Lacy asked.

"Captain, that's his name. At least that is what they call him. Well, he promised to pay my way through University. And you know I need the help."

"Yes, you do, but not in selling yourself to a married man."

"You are so right," Shari whispered. "That's exactly how I feel, as if I sold myself. What am I going to do?"

"Don't call him again for starters," Lacy instructed.

The room went silent for a moment.

"I just walked here in tears to spill my guts to you, and you are holding out on me."

"You have always known me, haven't you?" Lacy asked, smiling.

"Yes, and you, me. So, tell me, what is it?"

Lacy knew that with Shari's present disappointment, her friend had no more room for another, but she also knew it made no sense hiding what she had to say.

"I am leaving, Hun."

"Leaving what?"

"Not what," Lacy continued. "I am leaving for abroad. My aunt got me into a College over there, and I am going to live with her."

Shari was truly happy for her friend. The fact that one of them was leaving from a lane to an avenue had no bearing on who did so first.

"I am happy for you. You know that, right?" Shari expressed emotionally. "But someone else I love is leaving me again. Will I be all alone?"

"No, never. I may not be here physically, but you will always be my friend. I will always take an interest in your life, always. We will make it, and we will do it together."

These words were Shari's confirmation that she was not alone.

"Promise me that no matter what happens, you will never let my parents know about my mistakes."

"What do you mean whatever happens?" asked Lacy.

"I am just saying. Just promise me"

"I promise," Lacy confirmed. "You mean a lot to me. We argue and disagree at times, but we always have each other's back. So, I got you on this one."

With that, they embraced.

Shari wanted so much to contact Captain, but she held her ground and did not for the rest of the week. She kept her phone close but promised herself not to answer if he called. She knew she wasn't strong enough to resist his melting words, so her only way out was to not hear his voice at all. She strived on the comforting advice of Lacy and knew she must take control of her life as planned, even more than ever.

Shari gravitated toward getting a job and wasted no time in mailing applications. She even took the time to drop off a few as she believed putting a face to a voice would be of interest to some employers.

As the week progressed, she drowned herself in her thoughts and waited for calls she hoped would be positive, so when she received a private call, which was not normal for her, she gladly opted to receive.

"'Hello, good afternoon," Shari answered.

"Hi, boo."

Shari recognized the voice she thought she would never again hear. She thought about hanging up but froze in fright.

"How may I help you?" she said.

"See me please, that's how."

"You have the nerve asking me to see you after what you put me through."

"What? What have I put you through? You are overacting."

"Your wife coming; is that not reason enough to react?" replied Shari.

"I did not know; it was not planned. I explained this to you already. Please just see me and let us sit and talk. I miss you."

There it was again-Captain's smooth welcoming words. What do I do? What do I say? Shari struggled with the voices in her head- Laci's advice vs. Captain's assurances. She struggled to keep her happiness a priority but failed.

"I will see you. For the last time though."

"What about tonight? Please boo, I can't wait any longer."

"Tonight. Meet me at the same place."

"Is six ok?"

"Yes, that's fine," Shari said.

"Should I send the same taxi for you?"

"No, I'll get there on my own."

"Ok, boo, see you then."

Shari sat rigid for a moment contemplating how she would break the news to Lacy. She worried that this time her closest friend would turn her away, for making yet another mistake. She would be left alone in her pain. But she just could not bring herself to say no to Captain. After all, she was in love with him. That fact, along with her feelings triumphed over any hurt she would face.

Shari was now at the restaurant waiting for Captain's arrival. She felt butterflies in her stomach, her heart pounded as if she was seeing him for the first time, but there was something different this time around, she just could not put her finger on it.

Captain's vehicle pulled into the driveway. She stood up and walked towards the vehicle, opened the passenger's door and settled in.

"Good evening," she said.

"Good evening, boo. Wow, beautiful as usual." He attempted to woo her with a compliment.

"No reason for the flattery," she countered.

"Not flattery if it is true. You always look beautiful. Why are you so angry, boo? Please understand I did not know my wife was coming home."

"Would you have told me if you did?"

"Of course. I wouldn't hurt you, never in this world. I miss you so much, believe me."

He leaned across and drew her face towards his. As he kissed her, she pulled away.

"Please boo, I need you. Forgive me and let it flow. Let this flow."

Shari sat in silence as he drove off. She noticed he was heading in the direction of his home. She needed to say something; she wanted to ask him where the hell he was taking her or just shout for him to stop the vehicle. The memory of him pressing up against her and the scent of his skin overpowered her need to end things. So she sat still and allowed him to once again take her to his den of

101

passion. This time was no different from the last, except there was no wine drinking or the distraction of viewing a movie. She found herself so deeply wrapped up in everything that he had to offer.

Shari had experienced newness like never before. The thought of ever losing him or being out of his arms became her greatest fear. He was her savior, her hope, her love. He was her life, and she did everything in that moment to show him she felt just that. The night repeated itself, as Captain had hoped.

"I am your property now, aren't I?" she whispered.

"Time to admit the fact that we need each other," he said.

"Your wife is coming home."

"Yes, but that doesn't change the way I feel about you."

"I have fallen in love with you, and the fact that you belong to someone else makes it much harder."

He pulled her close, as he knew the feel of his body was something she found much comfort in.

"I need to go," she said.

"Please stay a bit longer."

"No! Your wife will be here in a week. This should not have happened. Either you call the taxi or I will."

It was now clear to Captain that she was in a no-nonsense mood and he did not want to be the reason for any more discomfort. So, he did as she requested without saying another word. She left with tears flowing. She felt as if she had allowed herself to be a part of an unfinished game. She tortured herself by inflicting pain on herself. She thought of how much she needed Lacy right now. Even though she often questioned her decisions, she knew she really cared about her, but Lacy not being there physically, did nothing to comfort Shari.

Without a comforter, Shari knew healing from the hurt would not be easy. No one would fully understand, so she dealt with her mistake alone. She became a stranger even to herself. Her parents tried to figure out the change in their warm-spirited Shari but doing so left them with more questions than answers.

Shari felt alone in a world where her thoughts were her only companion.

***

It was now a month since she had made her second mistake with Captain. The fact that she had not heard a word from him was evidence that his wife had come home. He seemed to have distanced himself from her, and every day she still listened for her phone to ring to once again assure her that she was in his thoughts. But the call never came.

All interest for the future was swept away, because if Captain was not a part of her life, then there was no life to live. She cried herself to sleep at nights. The loss of Captain took a toll on the vibrant spirit she once was, but she could not help to think that something else was going on with her, because of how ill she was feeling lately.

It was as if she was fighting a rare illness.

Shari could not hide that the little mouthful of food she ingested daily did not lie still in her stomach. She knew she could not tell her mother the real reason for her absence from life. Her mother never asked questions, so Shari only asked her mom to make her a cup of mint tea when she believed she was at her last wit.

"Mom?" Shari moaned.

"Yes, mi chile." Her mother entered her room to find a pale-looking Shari curled up on the bed. "Is wah wrong wid yuh?" her mother asked.

"I just don't feel well. Can you make me another cup of mint tea, please?"

"Of course, but I don't like how yuh look innuh. Yuh sure yuh don't need to si a docta?"

"No. I'm ok."

Her mother walked off to make the tea, and Shari clenched her fists, fighting to conceal how she truly felt. Her mother soon returned with the hot tea. Shari pulled herself up on her bed to receive the tea. She sipped once but realized something was wrong. She tried to hide her discomfort by telling her mother she was feeling much better and just needed to lie down a bit.

Although her mother was concerned that Shari opted for the bed, she took solace in the fact that she was feeling better.

"OK, my darling. Mi going to look something for dinner, but I will do it quick. A soon come back."

"Thank you, mommy. I'll be fine," Shari replied.

As soon as her mother left, Shari hurriedly got off the bed and ran towards the bathroom but did not reach in time. She could not control the unsettled feeling inside her stomach. She vomited the tea and anything else that cared to follow. She began crying. She was alone facing something she did not know how to explain. Her only friend had left, and the man who told her he would always be there had not seen it fit to pick up the phone and call. Her mother had to be kept in the dark as Shari would not be the reason for her disappointment.

She suddenly remembered the money Captain had given her to get herself a gift. She now had a different need for it.

As soon as her mother returned, Shari smiled, convincing her that all was well and that she really needed to hang out with friends tomorrow. Her mother welcomed this news.

"That's good dear. See what real old mint can duh, yuh will soon be yourself agen."

Shari smiled, "Yes, mom, I see."

"I am making stewed peas for dinner. I know it is your favorite."

Shari felt sick again but smiled.

"Mhmmm, yes, it is."

She got up the next morning and made sure she tidied her room, even though that too had become a struggle. She would not leave her mother to do this. It was now 7 am, and with no appointment at the doctor's office, she wanted to be one of the first in line. Shari left home giving her mother the impression that she was meeting friends.

"Mom, I'm off."

Her mother walked towards her and stared at her with concern.

"Why does yuh skin luk suh pale? Yuh sure yuh want to go out today?" her mother asked.

"Yes, mom, I am fine. Fresh air may just be the thing for me."

"Good to si yuh outa di bed. Be safe."

"I will, mom."

Shari headed to the bus stop and was relieved when she got on public transportation right away; it was becoming difficult for her to stand for any length of time. At the doctor's office, she waited patiently, but the fact that she was experiencing dizziness did not go unnoticed.

"Miss, are you OK?" the nurse asked.

Shari was away from home and free to express how she really felt.

"No, I'm not. I feel as if my life is leaving my body."

"Let me tell the doctor, so he can see you right away."

Shari was granted permission to see the doctor ahead of the other patients. It was obvious to everyone present that she needed to be attended immediately. As she walked into the doctor's office, she fought the mixed thoughts running through her mind. She was convinced she was fighting a rare disease and braced herself for the news of no cure for such.

"How are you today, young lady?"

"Doctor, I do not know. I have not been feeling well, and I seem unable to keep down anything I eat. "

The doctor lifted her chin and peered into her eyes.

"When was your last period?" he asked.

Shari struggled for an answer. "I don't remember."

She wondered what her period had to do with the way she was feeling.

"That's OK, my dear," the doctor assured her. "It is my job to find out what is wrong. To do so, I have to rule out things I think might be contributing to your poor health. So, I am going to give you a stick—let's call it that for now. Go to the bathroom and pee on it. In five minutes, return it to me please."

Shari was puzzled but knew she needed to feel better.

"Ok, sir."

As she went into the bathroom and pulled the stick from the wrapper, she noticed that it resembled a pregnancy test. She quickly dismissed this as she recalled the doctor's words of elimination. She followed his instructions carefully and waited for five minutes before she picked it up. She opted not to look at it, as she returned it to the office and handed it to the doctor.

"Ok, let me see here."

The doctor briefly stared at the gadget, as if making certain he had not misread it the first time.

"Young lady, how old are you?"

"I am eighteen years old."

"And who do you live with?"

"My parents."

Shari was now convinced that some rare disease was her hurtful reality.

"Well, I have found the reason for your discomfort," the doctor said.

As she braced herself, the doctor took her hand and calmly told her.

"You are going to be a mother."

"What!" she exclaimed.

"Young lady, you are pregnant."

Shari knew what she was hearing but did not understand what the words meant.

"What? How can that be?" she cried.

"Young lady, you are old enough to know how it happened. At this point, I am unable to tell you how far along you are since you cannot provide me with the date of your last period. Would you like to call either of your parents?"

"No, thank you, I will be fine."

"I can see this is not something you had any plans for, so I will advise you to let someone know as soon as possible."

"Yes, I understand. I will," she said. "Thank you, doctor."

"You take a little time to process this. I want you to come back and see me in two weeks... or visit a doctor with whom you are comfortable, but make sure you see a doctor in two weeks."

"Yes sir, thank you."

Shari held on firmly to the arms of the chair for well-needed support. The news of battling some generic disease would have been welcomed compared to her present reality. There would never be any form of redemption from this betrayal to her parents.

She walked numbly out of the doctor's office and headed straight towards the door.

"Miss, excuse me, this way to make payment."

"I'm sorry," Shari apologized. She was so dazed; she had forgotten to pay for the visit.

"Are you OK, miss?" the nurse asked concerned.

Shari nodded. "Yes, I'll be fine."

She managed to board the bus to go back home. As she walked through her lane, she now had a renewed awareness as to how and why poverty had gripped the individuals living there. She also noticed that they had found comfort in the fact that they had found a dwelling place. She saw a few girls sitting on the corner, one of whom had dropped out of school early and had become a mother. Shari stared at her, as she realized she was a child herself.

Shari saw failure, hurt and pain but most of all hopelessness, and thought to herself: "I will never live like this. I will never bring a child to live like this. I will never be you."

As she got home, and made her way to her room, her mother called out.

"Is that you mi dawta?"

Shari knew once her mother saw her, she would know something was wrong. So, she made sure she did not come to her room.

"Yes, it's me, mom. Just going to lie down. Talk to you later."

"Lay down agen? Don't yuh feel betta?"

"Yes, but the walk has made me a bit dizzy. A little rest and I'll be fine."

"Ok," her mom replied.

Shari's day quickly became night. She thought of Captain and the broken home he was about to fight to repair. She thought of herself and saw her broken dreams and a lifetime of regret. Most of all, she thought of her unborn child.

She could not see beyond that.

Whatever the outcome, whatever decisions to be made, she could do nothing without Captain's knowledge. They both played a role in defying thirty years of marital vows. She thought of every reason not to contact him, as she knew his wife was now at home, and there was no way he would come out to meet her. She also knew that she could not go through this by herself. If anyone would be able to help and give her insight to the first step towards a solution, it would be Captain.

Shari pushed her fears aside and called him.

It was the first time she could truly admit that she was nervous and frightened about contacting her beloved Captain. Her hands began to sweat as she hesitantly dialed his number. She prayed with her whole being that he would take her call.

After the third ring, her breath gushed from her lungs as she recognized the voice at the other end of the line.

"Hello," Captain answered.

"Hmm, hello," Shari replied.

"Shari? Why are you calling me here, now? Don't you know my wife is home? Are you trying to make trouble for me?"

"What? No! Why would I want to make trouble? Don't you think I would have done that long ago? There is something you must know."

"Honey, where are you?" Catherine echoed.

Coming dear. I'll be there in a minute."

Shari's heart melted, as she heard the dedication Captain had towards his wife. Just weeks ago, he had shown that same level of warmth towards her.

"You see why it is not a good idea to call me here," he half-whispered.

"OK, it isn't, so can we meet to talk then?"

"My child, you are even crazier than I thought."

Shari could not understand the sudden change in his attitude towards her. She knew it would be a bit difficult for him to spare time for her now, but she could not comprehend his hostility.

"Crazy, Have I ever used an unkind word towards you?" Shari shouted.

"Look, my intentions for you are pure, but my wife has no idea about us, and I intend for it to stay that way. We had two great experiences together, but please that's all it was, and that is all it can be now.

Catherine came to tell me she is returning home. She is just putting her priorities in place. I guess it will be sooner than we planned for."

Shari realized that now was the time to inform Captain of the responsibility he had on the way; one that would be a part of the rest of his life.

"You are so right about 'sooner' than being planned because the child you have on the way fits that phrase very well."

"What the hell are you talking about! What child?"

"The one I'm carrying. That's right, I'm pregnant! I found out today."

"Congratulations, my dear. The child's father must be proud. Have you told him as yet?"

"What are you implying? Are you denying you are the father?"

"You must be crazy! I know I'm not. Don't you think I knew exactly what I was doing with you? Do you think I would be so careless, to not take every precaution to prevent this from happening? Listen to me! I will not allow you the mere thought of breaking up my home with your lies. Are you trying to shake me down for college support? You best crawl back in your hole. Whatever you seek, I suggest you look elsewhere. I hope you find the real father of your child, and I wish you all the best of luck. Do not try to contact me again, or you just may regret it."

Shari gasped for air. She could not relate to the words she heard from the man who told her he would always be there for her. She then recalled and understood the wink shared between Captain and his neighbor. She was just another of his protégés, his conquests, his experiments. He had no intention of helping her, and he had never seen beyond her physical appearance.

With a sob in her voice, "You said you took every step to prevent this from happening, but did you ever think for a second, how to prevent me from being hurt?" Shari asked

"Goodbye, my dear," Captain replied.

And with that, he was out of her life. He was the only one who was in the position to help with her child—their child. If he did not accept his responsibility, then she would have no other way of proving he was the father. Getting a DNA test would require money, and she had none. The same thing that would play a huge part in caring for her child anyway, and she saw no other means of getting any. The thought of her parents or anyone in her community finding out she was pregnant for a married man placed a heavyweight on her heart and conscience. She had no way to ever come to terms with either.

She was often picked on for behaving as if she was above everyone else, even though she simply aimed to hold her chin up and fight her way through, which was the very thing her parents taught her to do.

She couldn't bear the thought of never entering college or bringing a child into this world that would never know its father or the joy of having a happy childhood. In her mind, she replayed every word Lacy tried hard to get across to her. The only thing she had left to give to anyone—especially a child that had not come into the world as yet—was disappointment. Within that instant, Shari decided that her existence only caused others pain.

Life as she knew it was over, so if she checked out a bit early, it would only give everyone that mattered to her an early start in getting over the fact that she no longer existed. She became her own judge, jury and executioner. She convinced herself this was the right thing to do. Shari got up from her bed and with a blank stare, tied together two scarves her mother had given her on her last birthday.

As she put into action her devious plan of taking her own life, thoughts of the pain she would leave her parents flashed through her mind. She felt the pain her mother would experience once she realized she had lost her daughter, her only child. But for her to live with what Captain had done to her would not be possible and she refused to go any further with this horrible feeling.

Shari silently begged the Lord for his forgiveness for what she was about to do. She knew she had to let her parents know the love she had for them, so she had to leave a note behind:

A Man's Game

Dear Mom and Dad,

Please know this has nothing to do with either of you. You both have loved and given me all you had to give. I thank you for raising me as best as you could. Please don't cry for me. I will be at rest, as I could not manage to carry the burden I was now faced with. I chose to let someone into my life that did not deserve to be there. I chose to give him total control over me. I chose to open the door which you both fought so hard for me to keep shut. Please know my sad ending will be another's life-changing story, so one will live on because of me. I love you both so much. Please forgive me.

Shari placed the note on her bed. She tied one end of the scarf to a piece of steel that protruded from a bit of wall inside her room. As the tears flowed, she stood on a chair and tied the other end of the scarf around her neck. With all her thoughts now gone, she stepped from the chair.

The struggle for relief was lost in seconds and silence overtook the atmosphere... Two lives sacrificed for the happiness of others—for the happiness of a man who betrayed them both.

******

How many of us have lost our fellow sisters in this manner? So many times, we waste away pining over how

115

differently we could have done it all. We wonder if we will ever get another chance to relive that experience, and if we do, will there be a different outcome.

It is up to us women to choose our paths, to create our destinies, to decide how much power we allow men to have over us. So many times, we are left with the question of whether or not we chose wisely, and if this nightmare we find ourselves trapped in, is based merely on the fact that we have made a dreadful error in the choices we have made.

The damage is already done, the pain has been inflicted and the wounds remain wide open awaiting healing. No more regrets, this will be our time of recovery. We will not allow our tears to be in vain; we will not allow our hurt to find refuge in our hearts, and never again will we play dead while men claim victory over our lives. We will find our way back from the hurt, the pain, the brokenness, and we will ensure our efforts and sacrifices will not be in vain.

Some women may have contemplated suicide or may have committed the act to escape the emotional trauma. Even though death seems like the easy way out, it blocks the possibility of new beginnings and denies God's ability to extend grace even in our biggest mistakes. If you can relate to Shari's experience in any way, remember that there is always light at the end of the tunnel and there is no hurt too painful for God to heal. You can bounce back!

A Man's Game

If you can't relate to her experience, extract the lessons and guard your heart and body from men like Captain.

Questions:

1. Can we truly say anyone won in this case?

2. Can anyone be truly happy when a life is taken, especially because of a broken relationship?

3. How will Captain live with himself after finding out he contributed to Shari taking her own life, and in the same breath shattered the chance of her family ever experiencing happiness again?

4. Was Shari too naïve to believe that there was any future for her with Captain, and should Captain have risked breaking up his marriage to save Shari's life, or should he have told her the truth from the very beginning?

What are your thoughts?

3.

The Wrong Boy Next Door

Beth's first real experience with men began at the age of sixteen.

She was brought up to appreciate the fact that life would never come easy unless she worked hard for what she wanted. And living with nine other siblings made it even more difficult for her to visualize her goal or work towards attaining it. If there were a million definitions for the word 'poor', then Beth's family would be affiliated with each.

She believed that being the ninth child lengthened the wait of ever getting a chance to be ahead. Her mom and dad insisted that they would all fight the battle of overcoming poverty until someone got the opportunity to make a way for the rest.

Beth's eldest sister left home at the age of eighteen; she had insisted that her decision for doing so was solely because she fell in love, but Beth believed that even if that were not the case, she would have gone with the first person that asked her. However, Beth took solace in the fact that there was one less mouth to feed. They all had to go to school, whether or not lunch was provided or a hot meal would be awaiting them on their return.

Beth was a child of God; it has been three years since her baptism, but she was yet to feel fulfilled in her walk with God. She had somewhat accepted this feeling, though she knew she had only made the decision because her best friend Jennifer asked her to. Besides, the desire to explore the crushes she had on her peers took precedence over the will to serve God. Nevertheless, she pretended that He was her priority, even though for the three years she attended church nothing truly changed; except that she felt more connected to the earthly treasures of the world, even more than before.

She and Jennifer— who was also a child of God—used the church as a cover, while they regularly attended the many parties that took place in their community. For Beth, staying at Jennifer's house was like moving up to new sites. She was not as popular as Jennifer, and she needed to stay close to her to be noticed. They both found scouting boys to whom they dedicated love letters, a satisfying hobby. Jennifer proved she was a great dancer by always being able to attract a crowd wherever she went to have fun.

I recall Beth telling me of one specific occasion in which they both attended a party in the so-called Uptown spot, which happened to be a place with which Jennifer was very familiar. They were excited, as they knew they would be seeing many of their peers. However, that evening somehow took an unpleasant turn.

The vibes were high, and Jennifer could not resist a chance to do what she did best—dance. She did dances that Beth and most of their peers didn't even know existed. All attention was on her creative moves. Everyone peered around inquisitively to see what all the fuss was about. When they finally saw what was happening, they erupted with excitement. Jennifer stole the show; she was now guaranteed to be on everybody's lips for many days to come.

The following day, word about her actions had already reached the church. Beth was also identified as a main character in the shenanigans, even though she had only watched. After being reprimanded by her mother and the Pastor's wife, she was told that Jennifer was a bad influence, and she must part ways with her immediately.

She fought hard to deny that request, because to her, Jennifer was her only link to being recognized by the cool crowd. Regardless of her efforts, the stigma of Jennifer's infamous behaviour surrounded them both and eventually ended their friendship. Beth continued to pretend that she was putting God first, even when her actions proved otherwise.

She was now back at home, one not as glamourous as Jennifer's and way more crowded. She was now back with seven others including her mom, dad, and two nieces; everyone else had left to take on life for themselves. She knew that when it was her turn, things would be no different. She wasn't doing well in school and watching her family struggle through life had taken its toll on her. She wasn't looking forward to graduating, because she had no idea where she would go from there and she was convinced she had not done well on her exams.

Dan, a 21-year-old University student from the country, had just moved in across from her. His brother, Dave and cousin, Marcus were already living there, but apart from the usual salutations, Beth was not familiar with either of them. So, when Dan came to live there, Beth expected it would be the same. She was told by her sister Donna, who was better associated with them, that he had been accepted at the University to commence studies, and so he had to relocate to the area.

Since Dan's home was one, she had to pass every day, Beth knew she would get a chance to see what he looked like. She did not appear anxious, even though her sister boasted how extremely handsome he was. One thing that did catch her attention was that other young ladies quickly became friendly with him and tried hard to get his attention, and he didn't waste time in praising himself for being their centre of attraction.

Beth finally received her examination grades and, as expected, she had done very poorly; so much so that she was fearful of telling her mother. She didn't want to add more worry to her mother's already uneasy life. She tried to take solace in the fact that a few of her other siblings started to find good jobs, which helped to ease the burden of her parent's daily woes. However, she had no plans for her future, but she knew she could not give up at this point. She made the difficult decision to inform her mother of her failure, even though she was fearful. Beth knew her mother would try to understand since she had always understood the challenges they faced growing up.

She and her siblings all went through school enduring days and nights of hunger. Even though some of them managed to find success despite the circumstances, her mother knew they weren't all made the same. Her mother knew that there would always be room for mistakes and failure, but she had taught them never to yield.

So Beth decided to show the results to her mother, and as Beth hoped, she was very understanding. Her mother told her that she would have to stay home for a while and try to find a continuing class, so she could re-sit her exams. She appreciated her mother's understanding, so she applied to a part-time program in an institution that assisted students who completed the program, to find employment.

Applying was the first step, followed by doing an entry test. It would take some time after both to find out if she was successful, so Beth knew she had time on her hands since she would be home. Although she dreaded staying at home, she knew no other alternative existed at the moment. This time she would have to concentrate on being successful.

Beth continued to attend Church and distracted herself from anxiously awaiting her results by spending time with God. She would often pass by Dan's house, and soon began receiving salutations.

She believed that his sudden greetings were a part of a schedule he came up with to ensure he would not miss her passing at any point in time. She, however, responded to him out of courtesy, even though she had only been responding to a voice and not a face. She often wondered if she would ever get the chance to see who that voice belonged to. She, however, thought this would not come easy, as Dan would always hide in the dark of his porch as if he wanted her to anxiously await his big reveal.

Beth recalled seeing Dan leave on many occasions for school, but without getting a glimpse of his face. She tried to convince herself she was not interested in him, but she just could not help feeling anxious to see what he looked like.

She recalled the night her thoughts, hopes, feelings and whole life changed. She was on her way home from Church and expected to be greeted by one of Dan's usual salutations. But this time he had different plans. As Beth walked slowly passed his house, she was greeted.

"Good night, lovely lady. How was church?"

"Blessed. How about coming to receive some of the blessings?" Beth replied.

"I just might, since I am being officially invited, but can you let me know exactly what to expect when I visit?" Dan asked.

"There is no expectation when anyone comes to church. You just come and ask the Lord to work through you," Beth replied.

"I understand, but can you sit with me a bit and tell me more about your church?"

Beth realized that she was being asked to tell someone about Jesus, and all He could do for them. The fact that she was uncertain that she believed Jesus was even her answer made sharing about him a bit hard for her.

But on the other hand, this was finally her chance to see Dan, so she accepted the invitation. She opened his gate and walked towards his very dark porch. He got up from the chair on which he sat and opened the grill to allow her inside.

"Welcome, Beth," he said.

"Thank you," she replied. "But I would feel much better if I could see who I'm talking to."

"Of course," he replied. "It's just that I enjoy sitting in the dark. I believe the dark gives you a better chance of seeing a beautiful angel of light."

She was amused by his flattery.

"Are you saying that I am an angel?" asked Beth.

"You must be," answered Dan. "I have not seen anyone as beautiful as you in a long while."

"Thank you," replied Beth, "but I am sure my beauty would be more visible if you view it in the light."

Dan chuckled. "Your wish is my command."

He walked over to the light switch and flicked it.

Beth stood speechless, as she now saw what her sister meant when she said how handsome he was.

He was very tall, slim built with dark-chocolate complexion, straight nose, beautiful brown eyes and nicely-shaped lips, but the thing that stood out the most to Beth was his handsome smile.

Beth felt as if her breath was being slowly taken from her. It became hard to hold her composure. Dan realized that for some reason she was finding it very hard to get a word out, so he helped her by being the first to speak.

"Now that I have seen you up close for the first time, I must say, you are exactly how I imagined - a beautiful angel."

She managed to mutter the words "thank you."

She decided it was best he did not know what she really thought of him, so she took care not to mention that she was captivated by his looks.

"Can you sit please, and tell me a bit about yourself, well apart from the fact that you are well dedicated to Church?" Dan said.

"Myself?" Beth replied. "Thought I was invited to tell you about who made this beautiful 'angel'."

"Of course, you were. But don't I first need to know about the one who is going to tell me about the Creator?" said Dan.

"No, you don't."

Her refusal was a way of not having to reveal too much about herself to Dan. Besides, she was already finding it hard to even sit with him, and being the shy individual she was made it even harder.

"OK, let me start," Dan said.

He took the time to fill her in on all that was going on with him in College, and how much he missed his country life. He said adapting to the change of atmosphere was proving difficult for him, as everything seemed different. He told her he wanted to be an Economist and was aware of the hard work involved if he was going to become successful.

He talked about how much he missed his younger sister, though he was apart from her for only a short time. Beth admired him for being so close to his sister. She noticed how distraught he seemed whenever he mentioned his nights of being alone because he was not involved with anyone.

As she listened to his life story, she tried hard not to mention anything about hers, because if she did, she knew she would have to mention the hardship she and her family had been going through, and she dreaded anyone knowing about that.

Her invitation to share God's words was hijacked by Dan sharing his story. She, however, found interest in this and lost track of time, until Dave and Marcus pulled into the driveway.

They were not astonished to see Dan with a visitor, but they were surprised to see who it was that had his attention—the girl who rarely spoke. As they both stepped from the vehicle, Beth noticed their smiles.

"Good night," they both said.

"Good night," Beth replied.

They glanced at Dan, giving her the impression that he had finally done what he had set out to do. The only thing left for either of them was to give him the thumbs up.

Beth felt some discomfort and told Dan she had to leave.

"Why are you going so sudden?" he asked.

"Remember, I stopped here right after church," she replied.

"I understand, but only if that is the only reason for you wanting to go."

"Have a good night Dan. It was nice talking with you. I guess we will be seeing each other more frequently now," she said.

"Yes, we will," Dan replied.

As she turned and walked towards the gate, she could feel his eyes on her, as if viewing a perfectly made sculpture. As she turned to close the gate behind her, she saw that it was more than just a feeling. It was as if he couldn't stop watching her.

"Well, good night again," she said.

"I enjoyed your company, Beth. Have yourself a great night. "Dan replied.

Beth walked along the dusty track to her house and could tell her arrival was being awaited because the lights outside were still on. She knocked on the door, and her mother opened it.

"Beth, yuh mean fi tell mi yuh jus coming in from church. Something keep that I don't know bout?"

Her mother was one to always worry about her children's whereabouts, and so Beth did not expect any different.

"No, ma'am. I was down by the bottom house."

"Which bottom house? Yuh mean di one weh those boys live? What yuh doing down there suh?"

"I just stopped to say 'hi." She replied

"Well, next time yuh come a yuh yaad fus. So nuh baddi nuh affi a wanda weh yuh deh."

"Ok mam," Beth replied.

***

The next day was as any other, except that Beth now knew exactly what the boy next door looked like. Although he was off to school, she knew she would be hearing from him later, judging from how well their night went. She recalled the lengthy conversation she had with him, and that was enough to put a smile on her face.

Beth, however, tried to understand the reason he had opened up to her with no hesitation, even though he was just meeting her for the first time. She, however, saw it as his way of appreciating her company and as a sign that he felt a sense of comfort around her.

It was already evening, and she looked forward to her mother getting in from work, as she knew a meal would be coming with her, as she normally brought something from the restaurant where she worked. And although Beth knew she would not be the only one to partake of the contents, she still appreciated whatever she got.

Beth finally saw her mother coming around the corner and noticed that, apart from her usual parcel, she had an envelope that immediately caught her attention. Beth could not hide being curious about the envelope her mother held.

"Ma'am, what's in that envelope?"

"Nothing that has to do with you."

Beth's instinct knew otherwise. "Is it the letter from the Institution? I know it is."

"Yes. And I am disappointed because once again you failed."

This time something was different. She knew it was her mother's way of happily telling her she finally got a break. And with that, Beth jumped up, tore open the letter and screamed as her eyes ran across the words: "You have been accepted."

"Yes, at last, another chance to get on track."

She couldn't recall being so pleased about any news she had received, and she could tell her mother felt the same.

"Well, a hope dis time yuh will achieve yuh goal."

"I will, Mom."

Beth knew this new journey would not come easy as she would once more be dependent on her mother to assist her with travelling expenses and lunch. This had never been an easy task for her mother, but Beth took solace in the fact that she had fewer mouths to feed, relieving her of some of the burdens she had to bear.

She was overwhelmed. She wanted—needed—to share this news with Dan, but they had only had one real conversation, and she would not be the one to initiate another. Besides, Dan was not one to shy away from making the first move at anyone or anything, so she knew she would get another chance with him.

At nightfall, Beth was inside with her family watching the small television, the centrepiece of their daily enjoyment. Her attention was directed towards the screen when she heard Dan's voice calling out to her. She sat still and quiet for a moment, making certain she had not misheard. This would be the first time he had come to her house. Although he was acquainted with her sister, he had never visited her home. For her, he had now made an exception.

Dan's voice echoed from outside for a second time as he shouted her name. Now she was certain she was not imagining. Beth got up and slowly walked outside.

"Where yuh going?" her mother asked.

"I'm coming right back, mom."

Outside, Dan came into view as she approached the gate.

"Hi. What brings you to my side of town?" she asked.

"I'm just in from school and was wondering if you could come to keep me company?"

Saying 'yes' would pose a problem because she knew her mother worried when her children were anywhere other than home at nights.

"Ok. I will be there shortly," she replied.

As she walked back inside, she wondered how she would tell her mother that she was stepping out for a while. She knew she would be bothered by this, but she also knew that she was of the age to make her own decisions. Besides, getting another chance to sit with Dan was something she could not give up--not even at the price of her mother's worries.

Beth built up the courage and informed her mother that she was going out to have a conversation with Dan, and as expected, her mother ranted about the dark, but Beth assured her that she would be fine.

As she walked towards Dan's home, there was no car parked in the driveway, which meant he was home alone. She smiled, recalling their first encounter.

Dan was on the porch waiting for her, and as she approached, her suspicion became apparent. He said he would be alone for the weekend because Dave and Marcus opted to spend theirs in the country. Beth was elated to hear this news, although somewhere in her mind she worried a bit about being alone with him. Nevertheless, they sat down to talk.

He offered her something to drink, but she declined. They talked for hours, and she told him about the many misfortunes' life had thrown at her, and how all of this had affected her success in school. She told him about her getting another chance at it.

Dan told her what he knew she needed to hear—told her it was the right time for her to go after her goal and make something of her life. Beth saw that Dan was smitten, but she also saw that time had passed.

"Oh, my Lord! Look at the time," Beth exclaimed.

"Just relax," Dan replied, "You could leave, but it's already Saturday, so let's sit and finish getting to know each other. As soon as it's light out, you can leave."

Since they were already in the living room, he invited her to lie on the couch and hurriedly assured her that he would take the floor. Beth was feeling a bit tired, so she accepted his invitation. Dan did little to allow her to get any rest. He began to mention how attractive he thought she was and even confessed his desire to talk with her the first time he laid eyes on her. "Dan, I am a part of the Church. I hope you remember that."

"So, because you are a child of God, you can't have feelings for another human being?" Dan asked.

"No, that's not it at all. But some things are just not allowed." Beth replied.

Dan laughed, and Beth wondered if he was mocking her or God. For a moment, she felt stupid and wondered if he considered her a lame guest.

But she tried not to give him any indication as to how she was really feeling and convinced herself the only thing to do was to listen. So, for the rest of the time, she tried as hard as she could but became noticeably tired, nodding off frequently, until she no longer heard his voice.

"Jesus Christ, Dan! You mean to tell me you did not think to wake me up?" Beth exclaimed.

"For what? You were tired, weren't you?"

"What do you mean 'for what'? It's almost sun out, and I did not sleep at home, remember?"

"Yes, I know, but you fell asleep, so I let you sleep."

"Let me out, now! My mother is going to kill me," Beth shouted.

"Kill you for sleeping? OK, call your mother, and I will explain to her," Dan replied

"No! It's OK." Beth snapped.

Dan did nothing to hide how ambushed he was by her frenzy. For her, explaining to her mother as to why she did not sleep at home, gave her every reason to panic.

"Dan, I have to go home now," she uttered as she hastily pushed her feet into her slippers.

"Ok, Beth. Again, I loved your company. Can't wait to see you again."

"Thank you," she replied, with a huge smile on her face, "I have to go."

She ran up the track towards home but this time she could not evade her mother's wrath.

"Where yuh you coming from this time a day?" her mother demanded.

Dan stood at his gate, and loudly laughed at the echoes of her mother's words.

***

A month has now passed, and it was time for Beth to begin classes. It took her mother much time and effort to put together everything Beth needed for school. Beth had somehow become a bit closer to Dan, despite the many explanations she had to be giving her mother. She found herself more relaxed around him and trusted him with thoughts she would never share with others.

Dan offered to take her to school on her first day, and his brother Dave was quick to offer his vehicle. Her mother accompanied her to the gate, feeling positive about her daughter getting a second chance at educating herself. She also wanted Dan to know that her presence would always be with Beth.

"Good morning, ma'am. How are you?" Dan asked politely.

"Mek sure yuh tek care a mi dawta," she replied.

"Yes, ma'am. She is in good hands."

He walked around to the passenger side of the vehicle and opened the door for Beth. She smiled. She knew he was trying hard to impress her mother.

"OK, Beth. May God guh wid yuh."

"Thanks, mom."

As they drove off, Dan began staring at Beth.

"Keep your eyes on the road," she said.

"Sorry. You look nice in your uniform, that's all."

"Thank you," she replied.

She giggled before reminding him to keep his eyes on the road for a second time. As they approached the school gate, Beth thought about how well designed and beautiful the school looked.

She stepped out of the vehicle and was instructed by a security guard to go to the other side of the building where other students were gathered. As she turned to thank Dan for his kind gesture, she noticed that he had a few admirers. The stares, giggles and obvious flirtations thrown at him were more than she could bear to see, especially on her first day at school. She slammed the car door in disgust.

"What?" Dan said.

"Nothing—I will see you later," Beth replied.

She walked away to join the growing number of students waiting to be addressed. She was drawn to four students standing together, all looking noticeably tired. It appeared as if they were waiting for a while.

Beth nervously began walking towards them but froze. One of the young ladies saw what was happening and walked over to meet her.

"Hi, I'm Caroline", she said "I can see that you are a bit nervous. Well, we all are but come on, let me take you over and introduce you to the rest."

"Ok, thank you. I am Beth," she replied.

Caroline took her by the hand and brought her to where the other girls were standing.

"Everyone, this is Beth. And Beth, meet Stephanie, Shannon and Nicola.

"Which Department will you be in?" Nicola asked.

"I am here to study Administration," Beth answered.

"So are we," Caroline exclaimed.

"Well, this looks like the beginning of a great friendship," Beth said excitedly.

And so, it was. For the next couple of weeks, the four were seen everywhere together. They had each other's backs and supported each other at all times.

Beth seemed happy and engaged with school, so much that it became very easy for her to walk past Dan's home every day without glancing at it. For him, things were not that simple. She was losing interest in him, or perhaps so he thought. So, he waited on her one day as she returned from school.

"Hi, Ms. Beth," Dan called.

"Hi, Dan," she replied as she continued walking.

He stepped off his porch and hastily walked out behind her.

"Can you hold up please and sit with me a while? I would like to talk with you."

"I have homework and need to prepare for school tomorrow."

"Please? It will not take long. Besides, I am quite sure I can assist you with any level of work you care to throw at me."

"Not this one," she said.

He took her hand and persuaded her to sit with him for a while. Dan's requests were ones she could not turn down, so she gave in to him. As she walked back to his porch she asked:

"Why am I here, Dan? What is it?"

"Why are you so angry? Did I do something?" Dan asked.

"Why would I be angry?" Beth replied.

"Are you jealous?" Dan asked.

She tried to hide her emotions, but it was too late for that.

"Is it that obvious?" she said.

"Yes, and I'm very flattered."

He leaned over to kiss her, and even though she was still upset with him, she did nothing to stop him. Instead, she drifted into his arms. When he took his lips off hers, she sat in awe! She felt confused, but certain that she liked the way it felt.

"Beth, I want to get used to this."

"What do you mean?" she asked.

"I like you a lot. You are so different from the others I've met. You are truly a kind-hearted person. You are ambitious, and I just know you will be successful. I have been looking for someone like you Beth, to start a true connection."

"What are you saying? All your words seem old and staged as if you've rehearsed them."

Dan laughed as if he found her entertaining.

"We have been acquainted for only a short while," he replied, "but I respect you, girl. I want to make things happen, with you being part of it all."

She was young and not very experienced, but his words sounded formulated as if she had heard them before but she decided to overlook the obvious.

Maybe she was too mesmerized by those brown eyes; maybe she hoped that his feelings would somehow be true. She wanted so much to believe, even if he was unable to deliver.

Dan hugged her and convinced her she would never regret giving him the chance to make her happy. In that instance, she was sure he would be her choice. But she knew Donna would never accept her decision; she saw Dan for the player he was.

Dan played his role quite well for the next couple of weeks. He made sure he was the one to take her to school, and they became seemingly closer. Beth felt comfortable and excited, as she introduced him to her friends, They made it known to Beth how handsome they thought he looked. She took time out of every day to call him from school with her friends anxiously listening in.

She never grew tired of hearing him tell her how much she made him happy and thankful that she made the "right choice." She even laughed about the fact that her friends seemed a bit jealous of her relationship with him. They often joked that they dreamed about him at nights.

Beth was happy.

Dave and Marcus had now caught wind of the news of Dan's relationship with Beth. She knew that once they were aware, Donna would be too. So, she braced herself for what was to come.

Beth's absence from church became the norm, and Dan was the reason for this. She had no intention of giving up time with him. Her mother became concerned about her withdrawal from church, especially because she was always the one trying to convince her to stay close to God.

One evening Beth arrived home from school intending to head straight to Dan's house, but her mother was awaiting her arrival.

"Beth, I have to talk to you." Her mother's tone was serious.

"OK mom, but can we talk later?" Beth asked.

"No, now!" Her mother replied. "Every day yuh come home from school, yuh jus drop di bag an nuttin else fi di res a di day. An why yuh stop guh church? Is dat young man. From yuh meet him yuh jus change. Yuh nuh have yuh head pon yuh body innuh. Him don't want nuttin good fi yuh or him would tell yuh to stay innah yuh church."

"Mom, I am still a part of the church. I just attend less, and it is not because of Dan."

"Yuh tink yuh sista nuh tell mi what is going on. Yuh gone inna relationship wid him. What yuh know bout him iihn?"

Beth was now sure everyone knew what she wanted to keep a secret. She wondered if Donna's concern about this was a sign of jealously, recalling her commenting on how cute Dan was.

"Mom, I am eighteen years old, and I know what I am doing. There is nothing serious going on between Dan and I."

"Nothing serious, and yuh behaving like yuh tail pon fire. When di disgrace come, a hope you alone can deal wid it. And since yuh seh yuh of age now, mek sure yuh nuh ask mi fi nuh money fi guh skool. Mek yuh bwoy fren look affa yuh now."

Before Beth could reply to her Mother's rant, Donna appeared.

"Am I hearing right? Are you involved with Dan?" Donna asked.

"Really, you have the nerve to ask when you told Mom I am," Beth exclaimed. "I don't know what you call 'involved'; we are just good friends."

Though Beth knew her, and Dan's relationship was beyond friendship, she would never allow her mother to feel let down in any way. Donna drew her aside, clearly with the same intent as Beth; Mother must never know.

"Do you know what you are doing? Dan does not appear as the type that will settle with only you. He is probably with you because you made yourself so available," Donna expressed.

"It's not like that," said Beth. "He is not seeing anyone else. And I believe he truly cares about me and what I want. You are only jealous because he did not choose you."

"Ah, Ah, Ah. Ah. Aweeee. Jealous he did not choose me?!" Donna exclaimed. "My dear sister, do not flatter yourself. Besides, he is much younger than I am. You can believe what you may, but all I can tell you is, be very careful."

Beth walked away carefully hiding her tear-filled eyes. She could not understand why the whole world was against her and Dan's feelings for each other. Why couldn't they see what she saw?

She knew he was a bit comfortable around other girls, but he was young and attractive. He had no control over how people saw him or chose to behave around him. What mattered most was the way he behaved around her, and it was always well executed, and for her, that was enough.

She was now sure she had to see him because she needed assurance that the predictions of her family would never come to light. She tried to compose her now uncertain feelings as she marched to his house.

He was awaiting her arrival. As she opened the gate and entered, he saw the look on her face, and it was not the one he was hoping for.

"What's wrong now, Beth?" Dan inquired.

She sat on the porch, placed her head on his arm, and looked up at him. Her eyes must have told him he should know her woes without her saying a word. He gently placed his lips on her forehead.

"Let's go inside," he said. " Let me hold you and give you the answer to all those lingering questions."

For the first time, she felt safe and sure that Dan's arms were the right place for her. She was now in a world that only consisted of them both, one filled with trust and love; something that she felt she was experiencing for the first time. To her, he was her only comforter—and he knew this.

He lifted her from the chair. He slowly kissed her as he walked towards the door, closing it as he entered the room. He laid her down gently and started removing his shirt.

She knew his intentions, but this was exactly where she wanted to be. He laid beside her, gently undoing the buttons on her blouse, as he caressed her gently.

She tearfully uttered, "It will be my first time."

In that moment, her experience of pleasure and pain was her confirmation of what love really felt like. She knew this was the only place for her.

Dan made love to her over and over; she felt emotions she only heard spoken about. Her laughter and tears became a part of her moment, she felt as if they were learning about each other all over again. She heard her groans echoing in the quiet of the room as she was lost in her feelings and Dan's arms. She then knew she could never let him go, not even at the cost of her mother's happiness.

They both fell asleep, but Beth was quickly awakened by the sound of keys opening the door.

"What's that? What time is it?" Beth asked.

Dan woke up startled. "What's wrong, Beth?"

"Someone's inside," she replied.

He laughed as he realized she had forgotten he lived with family.

"It must be Dave," Dan said.

His suspicions were instantly confirmed.

"Hey Dan, gone to bed so soon?" asked Dave.

Before Dan was able to respond, Dave pushed open the door and was surprised to see that Dan was not alone.

"Hey, bro," Dan called out. "Why didn't you knock first?"

"Sorry, bro," replied Dave. "I thought you were alone."

Beth laid still under the covers, as there was nothing else, she could do. Dave hurriedly left the room and closed the door behind him.

"Hey, love, do not worry about it," Dan assured Beth. "He did not see you naked or anything. Besides, I want everyone to know you are my girl."

"What time is it? I need to go home now."

"Go home?" Dan asked. "Aren't you going to spend the night?"

"You are crazier than I thought. I have school in the morning, and my mother will not be happy with this at all."

"You are eighteen now, Beth."

"Yes, but I am still under my mother's roof. Can I move in with you when she throws me out? I think not."

"Whaaaat, you did not even give me time to answer," replied Dan.

"No need—your silence said it all."

"It's eight p.m. don't you want something to eat?" Dan asked.

"Maybe early for you, but I came here at sun up. And no, I am sure my dinner is awaiting me."

As she got dressed to leave, she nervously pondered about having to pass Dave, who by now knew exactly what had taken place.

"Is your brother sitting in the hallway?" Beth asked.

Dan laughed. "Are you afraid to pass him? What are you embarrassed about? We did nothing wrong."

"That is easy for you to say. You will be seen as the one who 'scored.'"

He placed his palms around her face, making sure her eyes were fixed in his.

"This will never be about a 'score.' I will never hurt you. I waited for you, Beth, and now you're here."

He kissed her, placed his arms around her and escorted her out. She was not surprised to see Dave sitting on the sofa watching the television. She believed that was his disguise to make sure he verified she was the one coming from the room.

"Good night, Beth," Dave said as she walked by.

She responded faintly.

Dan accompanied her to the gate and watched as she walked the path toward home. The outside lights were turned off; it was not usual for her mother to do so early at night, but this time, Beth knew she was upset with her.

She knew she made her mother angry, but she also knew her mother loved her enough to never place her in any danger by allowing her to spend the night outside.

The next morning, she was afraid to ask her mother for travelling money. Dan would not be able to take her to school, and she felt nervous about asking him to assist her with cash.

"Why yuh don't gone to school yet? Is not me yuh waiting on fi money? Could neva because yuh a woman now, and yuh have a bwoy fren. Memba is dat yuh tell mi enuh."

"Mom, if it is to Dan you refer, he is not my boyfriend, and besides, he has already left for school."

"Yu si what a mean? Him gone to school, an don't even bada find out how you going to reach. Yu si when a talk to unuh pikni unuh don't listen. All I know is dat when di disgrace come, yuh kip it to yuh self."

"Mom, can I just get bus fare, please? I will do without lunch, but I have to leave now, or I'm going to be late."

"Unuh pickni nuh like hear di truth iihn? Tek dis. Is all mi have."

What Beth received would mean another day with only something to drink, but she was well-trained at making do with whatever she got. So off she went.

The journey was filled with lingering memories of her night. The feeling of Dan's touch was still fresh on her skin and in her mind. Her friends had told her about what to expect for the first time of passion, but no one ever gave her the true meaning of what she had experienced. She was overwhelmed by it all but wanted to keep her night hidden from her friends. She was not ready to tell it all, but her lingering joy took on the form of action. Her ear-to-ear smile was a giveaway to her friends that something was amiss as she approached them.

"Girl, I know you are glad to see us, but your smile says more than that."

Caroline's utterance got the attention of the rest. They all turned to see Beth's expression.

"Let me guess. You got an inheritance?" Nicole asked.

"What are you talking about?" asked Beth.

"Come on, girl, this is clearly a different you," said Caroline. "We know something, or someone is responsible for your sudden glow. Who or what is it?"

Beth hesitated to tell, but no words from her were necessary for Stephanie to figure her source of joy.

"Girl, you didn't!"

"I don't know what you are talking about," replied Beth.

"Yes Steph, what? Tell us," demanded the rest.

"Can't you tell what's going on with her? Beth is no longer a virgin."

The air filled with screams. Even though she did not confirm Stephanie's assumption, her silence did nothing to deny it.

"Wait a minute, I did not even know she was a virgin. Is there anyone else I should know about?" asked Nicole.

"Really, Nicole?!" Caroline blurted. "The rest of us are not on the topic right now—Beth is."

"Say something girl? Was it Dan? What am I saying? Of course, it was! Let me rephrase that, how was Dan?"

Beth placed one hand over her mouth in trying to keep her excitement from taking on the form of words.

"He was great!" she blurted.

"We knew it, it is true," said Shannon. "Oh girl, tell me, how did you feel staring into those gorgeous eyes, touching that well-shaped face, kissing those cherry lips?"

"Awwweeee!"

"Stop it, Shannon. Stop putting yourself in the girl's place."

"Who wouldn't? Just look at Dan," Shannon replied.

"Girl, we are happy for you but also care about you. Please just make sure you know what you are doing," said Nicole.

"What do you mean? Is there something you want to tell me?" asked Beth.

Nicole looked at Stephanie, who hesitantly answered, "No, nothing."

"All I am saying is, just take it slow with him. Make sure your head is in the right place." Nicole said

For the rest of the day, Beth could not help but replay Nicole words. She wondered why such a statement would come out if it had no meaning whatsoever. She knew they all had a crush on Dan, and that was a good reason for anyone to bring jealousy into play.

Beth's weeks turned into months, and she had no complaints about her relationship with Dan. He seemed to find the best ways to make it work. She felt more comfortable being his girl, mostly because her mother was less outspoken about her going by his house. His family saw her as a regular visitor and tried their best to make her feel welcome. She was sure that Dan had made good on his promise not to hurt her, and that was all she needed.

***

A Man's Games

Beth awoke for school one morning but felt like staying home instead. Her mother knew that she was never one to miss out on school, so she had a problem in allowing her to just rest, but she had to meet her obligations at work.

"Beth, yuh sure you will be alright?"

"Yes, mom, I am just a bit stuffed up. The flu is going around, so I bet that's what I'm coming down with."

"Awrite den, when yuh get up mek sure yuh drink some bush tea, and get someting fi eat. Yuh can tek two pill and rap up to try and sweat out di flu, before it fully attack yuh."

"Ok, mom, I will."

"Awrite. See yuh lata."

Beth went back to sleep and awoke to find it was afternoon. She was now sure that she was ill, as she had never slept this long before. She got up and thought some fresh air would help remove her cranky feeling. As she stepped outside, she saw Dan hanging laundry. She realized he had also opted not to go to school. Though a welcomed coincidence to spend time with him, when he turned and noticed her, he waved and went back inside, closing his door behind him.

Beth found this strange, as he would always jump at any chance just to talk with her. Perhaps he just needed a bit of space or was too busy, Beth thought.

In the evening, Dan was still nowhere in sight, as if he had spent the whole day inside. Beth's mother returned home to find her sitting outside.

"See, yuh feel betta."

"Yes, mom, I actually do."

"How yuh look suh, yuh sure yuh awrite?"

"I'm good, mom."

"Awrite. Si di food here."

Beth's appetite had vanished though she had not eaten at all.

"Thanks, mom." She replied

She got up again just in time to see Dan emerging from inside to sit on his porch. Beth saw that he was not alone, but she had a challenge seeing who was with him and she did not want him to believe she was spying. She, however, managed to see that his guest was wearing long, black hair-pieces. Beth thought to herself that something of that nature must cost a lot of money.

As they went back inside, Beth felt her world had been invaded by a man's thoughtless hurt, even though she had no idea who his guest was. Intuition told her it was not a relative because he had been quick to introduce her to his family. She tried hard to suppress her thoughts, but the thought of Dan keeping company with another female was unbearable.

As night crept in, Beth could not stop watching all activities that were taking place at his house. She finally saw Dave's car pull into the driveway. Dan and his female companion stepped outside to meet him. They all took a seat on the porch and entertained each other for a while.

Their laughs rang out in Beth's ear.

She watched as Dan and his guest rose, and she leaned over to hug Dave, so Beth assumed she was someone Dave already knew. Dan took his guest to the car and they drove off. Dave turned and looked in Beth's direction, so she quickly ran inside.

Beth was relieved that none of her family members had witnessed this, especially Donna. She now heard Donna and her friend's words echoing in her thoughts with greater meaning. Beth felt as if a piece of her soul had just been stolen.

It was now another day, and time for school. With a forced smile, Beth gave her friends the impression that her happy world still existed. They met each other at what had become their usual spot. They all hugged and asked Beth if everything was fine. Nicole wanted to know why she had not been in school yesterday.

"Nicole, give the girl a break."

"Really, Stephanie, I am just asking."

Beth felt something was being hidden from her.

"What are you hiding guys?"

Silence took over, as they all glanced at each other. Nicole bit her lips hard as if holding something back.

"Tell me, Nicole!" Beth insisted. "I can see that whatever it is, you are the one most affected."

"Shut up!" Caroline blurted at Nicole.

"No, no more," Nicole replied. "Beth, Dan have a girl up here."

"What? What girl?" Beth asked. "What are you talking about?"

"The other day when you opted not to take your call break, we went down to the lobby to make calls. While we waited for our turn, a girl who was before me in the line, was making her call. I happened to glance at the number she dialed, and it was one I knew, but I peeked again to be sure. And there it was, lo and behold, she was dialing Dan's digits."

"What? How would you know that? I never told you his number. Nicole, how do you know his number?"

"The same way I saw all the other's numbers they dial—peeking," Nicole replied.

"I do not understand," said Beth. "You must have made a mistake."

"We thought so, too," said Shannon, "but there is more."

"Really, Shannon, now you speak up?" said Nicole

"Shut up, Nicole! You can't keep anything in, can you?" asked Shannon.

"The girl must be told the truth," replied Nicole. "There is more, as Shannon said."

"Now when I told them what I had seen, they said that I was either wrong or lying or not sure, and that they needed confirmation. Well, yesterday they got all the confirmation they needed when we decided to take our call breaks together again. The same girl came but this time we were in front of her. I was the only one who recognized her and wanted to prove to the rest that I was correct. I stepped out of line to let her take my place and watched her dial... the same number yet again. I did not have to do much this time to persuade the rest of the gang I was right because they heard it for themselves."

"Heard what?" asked Beth.

"Her name is Gabrielle, and she started ranting about not getting Dan on his phone, and yes, she called him by name. She blurted out that it was weird that she had not seen you at school, which happens to be the same day Dan was unavailable to take her call."

Beth interrupted. "Are you saying this is someone who knows me?"

"It sure sounds that way, girl," Nicole replied. "We also overheard later on describing you to her friends."

"I do not understand any of this," Beth replied. "I do not have any other friends here apart from you guys. How could Dan know anyone here? I do not know what to believe right now."

"Beth, it is clear that Dan has a huge net over your eyes. Why would we make up any of this, when we know you will be hurt by it all?"

"Please, Caroline that is not what I am saying. I just don't understand where all of this is coming from."

"Well, I do. It's coming from Dan having another woman."

"Nicole can you just take a break with all your talking! You never know when to stop," said Stephanie.

"Oh yea, well at least she now knows the truth," Nicole replied.

"There you go again," said Stephanie. "Your mouth will eventually be the death of you."

"As long as it's for the truth," Nicole said.

"Beth, we are so sorry," Stephanie assured. "We see what this relationship means to you and know what this is going to do to you. But we are here, all of us, and if that girl thinks any of us is going to stand by and watch her fight you, she better make sure she takes Dan as her protector. And boy, that is what we are all hoping for."

"It's OK, guys," Beth said. "I know you all have my back, but I will figure it out."

The rest of the day was much different from any other. Beth did not do much talking; silence was the only comfort for her. Her friends tried hard to cheer her up, but nothing worked. She went home with a terrible headache, which made her mother suspicious, enough to begin wondering why her daughter was now frequently feeling ill.

"I'm fine, mom. It's just the level of schoolwork we got today."

"Ok Beth, whatever yuh seh. Oh, the young man from down the house come here calling yuh."

155

"For what?" Beth asked.

"How me must know? Mi look like mi know unuh young people business?"

"There is no business to know, and I do not have any time for him today."

"Mmm, yuh si I know someting nuh right. Yuh jus change all of a sudden. Yuh tail usually pon fiah fi guh down there, but now yuh saying yuh don't even have the time. A hope yuh know what yuh doing?"

"Mom, please. I'm going to shower and sleep."

"So yuh don't want nuttin to eat?"

"No, mom, I just want to lie down."

***

Beth awoke to another day for school, wishing she could stay away again and just sink her despair in her pillow. But she knew that would be a clear indication to her mother that trouble was truly around, so she pulled herself together and got ready for school. She prayed that she did not have an encounter with Dan, as she was still trying to figure out if the stories she had heard from her friends were true.

As her mother accompanied her to the gate, she saw that her prayers were not answered. Dan was sitting on the hood of Dave's car as if posing for a scene from the movie Grease.

Beth lowered her gaze to the ground intending to pass him without notice. Deep down, she knew his ego would not allow that to happen.

"Good morning, ma'am. Are you ready?"

She tried to ignore him.

"Ma'am!" he shouted.

As she turned to look she, she saw her mother was still standing at the gate. She knew if she did not stop to talk to him, then mom would have all the confirmation she needed for her assumptions.

"Ready for what?" Beth asked.

"I am taking you to school today"

"Are you now? How are you going to do that without being seen by Gabrielle"

He looked at her in confusion.

"What are you talking about?" he asked.

"Don't even bother. Your reaction just said it all."

"You said you were taking me to school. Can we go please?"

She had to put on the show of a happy morning, all for her mother's comfort. As they drove off, Dan demanded to know what she was talking about.

"You are playing me for the fool, aren't you? You pretend you have no clue what I'm talking about. Let me see you try and deny the woman that you had in your house the other day."

"What woman?"

"You are a real piece of work Dan. Are you really going to deny this? I saw her with my own two eyes, you saw me, and you avoided me for the whole day."

"Beth, I am not trying to deny anything. She was just my study buddy, Nadine. She always comes over before a huge test because we work well together. As for that girl, Gabrielle, I met her when I took you on your first day to school. She recognized me from my parish; turns out we are from the same place. We just exchanged numbers, because she needed assistance with a school project."

"Oh, my God! I do not believe a word you are saying," Beth shouted.

"Please, Beth, just listen. I need you to believe me before I leave." Dan pleaded.

"Leave… leave for where?" Beth asked.

"I wanted to tell you under less stressful circumstances," said Dan. "I am going off on the Student exchange program. I leave for New York for three months."

Beth's heart melted. She did not understand how the man that had just torn her heart to pieces could be the same one to pull her world from under her with the thought of not seeing him.

"OK, do what you must," she said.

"That's it? You don't even ask when I leave?" replied Dan.

"What does it matter? You leave when you leave,"

Beth was now in a nonchalant mood.

"Can I see you later, when you are home from school?" Dan asked.

"I don't think so," Beth replied bitterly.

"Please, I leave this weekend," Dan pleaded.

Beth looked at him with a sorrowful steer. But no words to spare. She stepped from the car. She tried to hurry since school had already begun, but she was interrupted by the tooting of Dan's car horn. She knew she had to hurry to get her name on the register, but she could not ignore that he wanted to say something. As she slowly walked back towards his vehicle, he opened the door and pulled her inside.

"Dan! What are you doing? I am already late for school,"

"No, you are absent from school," said Dan.

"What? You are making no sense."

"I leave in a couple of days, and you are mad at me. Do you really think I am going to enjoy my stay overseas?"

"Well, you should have thought about that before you decided to hurt me."

"I did, and I did not hurt you."

"Where are you taking me?" asked Beth.

"Home," replied Dan.

"I left for school. I can't just go back home."

"Yes, you can. I know no one's home, Beth, so you can just pretend you were at school. Your mom won't find out. I want to spend the rest of the day with you. Let me show you that you are the one that matters to me."

159

She was overwhelmed by confusion and uncertainty; unhappiness took on the form of tears which began streaking down her face. She had no more strength left to fight Dan, and she was uncertain if she even wanted to.

She rested her head on his shoulder as he pulled out of the schoolyard. She needed comfort and saw him as the only one to give it to her in that instance. He took her to his house knowing they would be alone, as his brother had left for work. To her, his intentions were clear, and even though his actions seemed another case of dejavu, she could not bring herself to pull away from him. He was what she needed to forget all her troubles. And she was prepared for all he had to offer. She stared into his eyes, hers filled with tears and whispered, "You've hurt me."

"Let me make it up to you," he replied and kissed her.

She once again experienced indescribable passion. This time, it felt as if it was for the very first time. All his lies seemingly became truths; for her, all of his sins were forgotten. Nothing said before mattered; she found love once more as if it were the first time.

***

It was now two months and two weeks of loneliness without Dan, Beth once again battled with the uncertainty of their love. She had yet to receive a phone call from him since he departed for his new adventure. Her friends now thought twice about having her back, as they were upset about her putting their advice aside and once more committing to Dan.

They told her that they would no longer be there for her when he hurt her again, and they assured her it would happen. It was all confusing to her because she didn't even exist for him anymore. The same man who said he would never hurt her. She tried to find comfort in telling herself that he must be missing her, as they both cried when he left.

The memories she shared with him were fresh in her mind. She kept replaying his words of wanting her. She concentrated on school, trying hard to hide that she was hurting inside because she knew her friends would be even more upset with her for pining over her beloved Dan.

She recalled taking a visit to the school nurse because of pain she was feeling but kept it a secret from her friends. They were worried and wanted to accompany her, but she convinced them that it was nothing serious. She was relieved to see she was the only student there, so she wasted no time in getting an answer.

Beth was escorted to a room, instructed to undress and be examined. The anxiety of discomfort was quickly replaced by the hope of being healthy. After a few minutes of unease, she was told to get dressed and wait for her results. She was told that she could return to her class if she wished.

Her need for answers would not allow her to concentrate on anything else, so she opted to wait. The nurse used this opportunity to educate her about the facts of life. It was as if the nurse was preparing her for something to come.

Beth knew her friends must be wondering where she was. She was worried they would come looking for her, so she got a bit flustered. The nurse tried her best to make her comfortable.

"We are ready, young lady." said the Nurse.

Beth sat with her legs visibly shaking, and her gaze locked on the diagnostic report in the nurse's hand. As the nurse looked down at the contents and up at Beth, she smiled, stepped closer and placed her hands in Beth's.

"What is it? Just tell me, please," said Beth

"I'm afraid you have genital Herpes," replied the nurse.

She was not aware of how bad that was, but she knew it was not something any person would want.

"What is it? How did I get it? What does this mean?"

"Calm down," said the nurse. "It does not mean that your life stops in any way whatsoever." The nurse did her best to explain the truth and dismiss any misconception Beth might have had. She asked how many sexual partners Beth had.

"Only one… ever", Beth replied. "I can't believe this is happening to me," she struggled to get the words out, "I am so young. My mother warned me, my sister, my friends, everyone warned me. How could I have been so stupid?"

"Hush, now. The good thing is that you know, so you can take control of what happens from this point onwards" comforted the nurse.

She assisted Beth in regaining her composure. Beth asked her if she could assist her in getting the rest of the day from school, as she knew she was not in any shape to face anyone.

"Yes, I will see to it. Go home and get some rest, and please remember you must set an appointment to see a doctor, who will advise you about how to move forward. I also think you should speak with the Guidance Counselor for additional support and help."

Beth sat silently for a while, trying to regain some strength before leaving for home. She knew her friends would be worried. She wanted to just get home without any of them seeing her, but her hope was short-lived.

They were waiting and immediately saw that something was wrong. They immediately bombarded her with questions.

"What is it, Beth?"

"Yes, why are you crying?" asked Nicole.

"Why were you in the Nurse's Office for so long?" Caroline chipped in.

"Please can we talk about it on Monday?" she insisted. "I just want to go home."

"Go home? But you can't go home like this."

"It's Dan isn't it?" blurted Nicole.

"There you go again, Nicole, always assuming. You don't even know what's really wrong." Shannon chipped in.

"What else could it be? He's the reason for all those tears."

Beth stood silent as she tried to process everything she had just heard. Her friends realized and took her to sit in the cafeteria.

"Girl, you need to tell us what's wrong, otherwise we can't help you," said Shannon

"Well, I already know what's wrong —Dan," said Nicole. "Beth, I can't say I feel for you this time. You were warned. Don't you see what he's doing to you? Are you going to wait until he destroys your life before you end things with him? We love you, but do you love yourself?"

Beth wanted to tell them, but pride prevented her.

"Well, since nothing seems to get through to you, let me enlighten you about a bit of recent information we've come across.

"Nicole, this is not the right time!" exclaimed Caroline.

"Why is it that I have to always be the bad guy , and open her eyes to reality?" asked Nicole.

"Because you can't help yourself." Replied Shannon.

"Say what you like, it is obvious she needs a babysitter, so I'll take the first shift. Maybe she has already heard, and that is the reason she sheds those tears." Said Nicole.

"Please, all of you," Beth interrupted. "Just stop talking—heard what?"

"Listen girl, a friend of mine is a classmate of Dan's 'mystery' woman, and she overheard 'miss mystery' mouthing off to friends about Dan being away from home and how much she misses him. She mentioned the numerous calls she received from him since he had departed, and the gifts he promised to take back for her."

This time Beth was certain Nicole was telling the truth, as she even mentioned where Dan had left for. But Beth also realized that she was the only one without a contact number for him while he was away. Embarrassment drove her to keep this to herself. This time was no different with Nicole, as she seemed to be the only one eager to share what she had learnt.

"Girl, we didn't want to tell you," said Stephanie, "because you were already going through something. We just did not want to add to that. But as usual, Nicole had no problem doing so."

"Sure right, I didn't," added Nicole. "And Beth, remember our Sports day is close. Invite Dan, and when he gets here, we are all going to gang up on him."

"Yea, yea do that, Beth. Let us beat him for the dirt bag he is," said Caroline.

"No," Beth argued, "he will get what is coming to him some other way."

"Surely not by you," mocked Nicole. "Every time he does you wrong, it is as if you reward him."

"Wait, so that means he is the reason you are once again crying. "What did he do this time?" asked Shannon.

"Girls," Beth cut in, "I know you worry about me, but this one I have to work out for myself."

"Aren't you going to tell us what's wrong?"

"It's OK, Caroline," Beth replied "I don't want to talk about it, not now. I have to go. I promise I will call you guys over the weekend."

"Yea right, you mean after Dan tells you what to say," blurted Nicole.

"Shut up, Nicole!" shouted Stephanie.

Beth was now sure her friends saw her as a sucker to Dan, and she did not want to continue. They all hugged her, and with tears in her eyes, she left.

She spent the evening wrapped up in bed.

The numerous phone calls from her friends went unanswered. She thought that explaining on Monday would be easier than hearing the "I told you so's." Food was the furthest thing from her mind, but she did eat; not doing so would make her mother think something was wrong. And she had no intention of explaining what it actually was.

She waited and hoped for a call from Dan, especially now that his actions had dire consequences on her, but his call never came. Beth was awakened by the sound of Donna's voice, calling out to her.

"What is it?" asked Beth.

Realizing that she had slept through the night.

"Was I really sleeping for that long?"

"Yep, so I guess you were tired," said Donna.

"Where is mom?" asked Beth.

"She left for the Market. Have you heard from Dan?" asked Donna.

"Nope, but I'm sure you have," said Beth.

"Me? Why would you think that?"

"Why are you bringing up his name now?" asked Beth

"Girl, I told you that boy was up to no good, and he's here," said Donna

"Here where?" asked Beth.

"Down by his house. He arrived early this morning but not alone"

"What do you mean?"

"He's with a girl," Donna said. "And Dave was the one that went to pick them both up."

"Girl? What girl? Maybe it's the same girl he told me he studies with." suggested Beth.

"You are so naïve. And besides, he is just getting back from abroad. What kind of studying would he be doing now?" replied Donna.

Beth hurried outside. As she walked towards Dan's gate, she saw that his doors were closed, and his brother's car was parked in the driveway.

"Let me tell you this, today is the day he is going to have to answer for the way he has been treating you because we are going to confront him."

"We? Who's *we*?" Beth asked.

"You will see," said Donna.

Beth knew a confrontation with Dan was inevitable and would be about much more than him bringing a girl over. Beth's pride would never allow her to make her situation known to anyone other than Dan. She immediately got back inside and began getting dressed. By now Donna was heading toward Dan's house. Beth called out to her, as she was in no way ready to face Dan under these circumstances.

As she ran after Donna, she saw someone leaning against Dan's wall. It was Arlene, Donna's friend. Beth knew they were both preparing for a confrontation with Dan. She knew she would be the only one able to stop what was about to take place. She watched as Donna angrily flew Dan's gate with her friend close behind.

"Dan come out here!" Donna shouted.

"Yes Dan, come out," Arlene demanded.

"Stop this please!" Beth sobbed.

"Shut up, Beth! You are too weak for this, but you are my sister. I will not stand aside and watch this 'player' use you."

Beth still tried to intervene.

Dan opened the door in a bit of fright. "What the hell is all this about?"

He soon realized something was amiss when his eyes caught sight of the piece of metal pipe in Donna's hand.

"Beth, what is going on here?" Dan asked.

She walked closer to his porch. As she tried to get a word in, Donna interrupted by pushing her aside.

"You let me deal with this Beth," she said.

"Deal with what? What is going on?" Dan asked.

"You are a wicked bwoy!" shouted Donna. "You think we believe you are clueless as to why we are all here?"

"What have I done? Beth, what did I do to you?" asked Dan.

"Bring out the girl you have inside?" said Donna.

"How is that your concern?" asked Dan.

"You know what, Donna," said Arlene, "why don't you call up the rest of your sisters and let us all give this boy a good beating."

"Who are you?" asked Dan.

"That is no concern of yours," replied Arlene. "Who is that girl you have in the house?"

"I do not even know you. What the hell is this?" Dan said.

Dave came out to see what all the chaos was about.

"Hi, Beth. Hi Donna. What's going on?" he asked.

"You are another liar," said Donna. "Why are you asking what's going on and every time Dan carries his call-girls here, you are the one that goes to pick them up? You stand by and watch your brother play my sister for a fool. You are a damn hypocrite."

"Let us beat him too," blurted Arlene.

"Stop! Everyone just stop!" Beth cut in. "Dan, what is going on? Who is she and why haven't I heard from you since you left? Why did I have to find out in this manner that you have returned?"

"Beth, I honestly do not know what you mean," said Dan. "Why is your family here to pick a fight with me? Whatever is happening, shouldn't it be between us?"

"You are right, and I need to talk to you," said Beth.

She convinced Donna and Arlene to step outside, as she wanted to speak with Dan alone. She knew now was not the time to tell him about what she had learnt from the school nurse, but she could not risk the chance of not telling him at all. As she stepped inside, Donna reminded her that his visitor was still there.

"It's OK, Donna. I will be fine." Beth said.

"Of course, you will, because we are right here," replied Donna.

"What is it, Beth?" Dan asked. "What is it that you had to bring your gang with you to tell me?"

"My sister is concerned about me, and I cannot blame her, because you've done me so wrong. Everyone now knows that I cannot look out for myself."

Dan stood in silence as if annoyed at the fact that he had to put up with Beth even being there.

"Dan, Dan."

He was being summoned by the hidden figure in his bedroom.

"I know she heard us talking," Beth said. "Who is she, Dan? How could you treat me with such a lack of respect?

I have changed all I believe in to fit into your world because I thought that would make you happy."

"Beth, you see what I mean?" Donna cut in. "Don't you hear the girl calling him? Dan, how can you be so disrespectful and wicked?"

"Please, I will sort this out Donna," Beth said.

Dave stood at the door as if guarding the mystery woman.

"Beth, you said you wanted to tell me something," Dan added. " What is it? I need to go."

"Go where—to her? Did I mean anything to you? Was any of what happened between us even real?"

"I care deeply for you, but did you really think any of this was forever? I did not mean to give you false hope." Said Dan,

Beth looked at him as if she did not recognize the person talking to her, nor the words coming from his mouth.

"Aren't you the one that told me you wanted to be wherever I am? Didn't you tell me you wanted to spend your life with me? Was any of that even true, are my feelings games to you? Did you make everything up just to lay with me Dan?"

Her words became jumbled, now mixed with tears. She lost herself and became unaware of the pitch her voice had suddenly taken on. "You said you never meant to give me false hopes. Did you mean to give me genital herpes?"

She covered her mouth in disbelief. The secret she fought so hard to keep was now in the open.

Dan became angry. "What the hell are you talking about?"

For Beth, the worst was now out, so why hide anymore she thought.

"You piece of shit! I went to the school nurse and she did some tests. I have herpes, and you and I both know you are the only one that could have given it to me."

"No, my dear, you got that wrong. I could not have given you anything, because I am clean," said Dan.

Donna started beating on the porch grills and demanded that he open it. Arlene joined in as they both flew into a fit of rage.

"You filthy dog! What the hell have you done to my sister?!" exclaimed Donna.

"Ask her what she has done to herself. I didn't give her no herpes."

Dave placed his hands on his head and stepped away from the door with no effort to hide his embarrassment and disgust for Dan.

Beth took this as her time to let her bottled anger go. She pounded on Dan's chest repeating everything that he had done to her. He grabbed her to block her blows. When she pulled away, she saw that the young lady was now standing at the door.

"Is that the girl?" Donna asked, "We told you he was hiding someone."

Beth stood in shock, as she was now seeing who Dan's mistress was, dressed in a sheer nightgown. Beth looked her over, then looked at Dan.

"I know you. Dan, Dan! I know this girl. She is one of the girls that I saw talking to you on the first day you took me to school. Oh, my God, this is the same girl my friends told me about; the same girl you said lived in your community whom you were just assisting with school projects. This is the girl that threatened to fight me if she found out I was at home with you."

"Oh suh Dan, you have her threatening my sister? Well, guess what? Since she opted to begin the fight, pull up this grill, and let the show begin. I knew you were a player, but I did not know you could be this cruel with your games," Donna ranted.

"Shut your mouth, Donna! You know nothing about me," Dan shouted.

Everyone was in shock to hear the silence was broken by his guest.

"Dan, is what she saying true? You gave her herpes?"

"Yes, he did," Beth confirmed, as she looked over at her. "And I guess that means you would have it, too, or maybe you gave it to him. Didn't you know he was involved with me?"

She said nothing.

"Didn't he tell you I lived right in front of him?" Beth went on. "You told your friends at school that you wanted to fight me. For what? For knowing Dan before you?"

"Leave her alone, Beth," Dan warned. "She has nothing to do with any of this."

"She has everything to do with this. She knew I was seeing you, and you knew I would be hurt by you bringing her here."

Dan walked over to his guest, threw his arms around her and escorted her back inside. He turned to close the door but that was blocked by Dave's foot.

"Hey, Dan, what are you doing?" Dave asked. "This is not the way mom brought us up. Is it true you gave her herpes?"

"I do not know if she has herpes, but I know I did not give it to her," Dan replied.

"You are my brother, but I will not allow this behaviour in this house. Are you trying to wreck your future? Herpes? How are you going to manage that and school?"

"Yow, bro, didn't you hear what I said? I know nothing about whatever she is talking about; as a matter of fact, I would like for everyone to leave."

"Yes, you would like that, right Dan?" Donna cut in. "Everyone and everything to just disappear, so you can pretend none of this happened. My sister will have to live on medication for the rest of her life, and that stupid girl you have in there will become another of your victims...

along with however many others there are, and she is acting as if she doesn't even care. You are his brother, you better talk to him or I swear I will tell all who wish to listen to what he has done."

"Donna, please," interrupted Beth. "Remember I am one of his victims. That means my business will be out in the open. I do not want that."

"Sorry to say it already is," Donna said. "Don't you think his girl is going to run her mouth at school? I hope she doesn't leave out the part where he must have it, too. My sister, listen, you made a mistake—that doesn't mean your life has ended."

"What am I going to tell mom?" said Beth.

"Nothing, she does not have to know, she has enough to deal with already."

Beth stood in tears, waiting for any kind of explanation from Dan. Dave asked everyone to calm down and allow Dan and his guest to leave in peace, as he did not see it fit for her to spend the rest of the evening. He assured Beth that he would get to the bottom of it all.

Beth agreed and asked Donna and Arlene to back off. Dave drove the car off with Dan and his guest inside, but not before telling Beth that he wanted her to wait because he needed to sit with her when he got back. She sat numbly on his porch and watched the car carry Dan and his guest off to safety.

She sat alone with too many thoughts crowding her mind. She could not understand how someone could change that quickly. She blamed herself for ever believing a word he had said and for allowing herself to get so attached. She knew she needed an explanation, but anything coming from Dan would not be the truth.

She thought of how hard it was going to be to live with what he had done to her. She had to put on one final show that would show him how much he had hurt her—and that she was not weak.

She got up from her chair, walked into his bedroom, and began going through his drawers. She gathered his clothes, as much as she could carry, threw them outside, took the sheets from his bed and threw them on the already high heap. She knew her memories of him sleeping with his sweetheart would never be erased from her mind. For now, she was satisfied destroying anything that she knew would hurt him. She knew exactly where to find his study guides.

He had just returned from overseas. She dragged the heavy suitcase outside and added it to the pile. Nothing she did now would take away her pain, but she knew Dan treasured material things, so destroying them would satisfy her.

After accumulating all she thought important to him, she stared at the high pile. For a while, she reminisced on every unkind word that came from his mouth. She went back inside and took up a can of gasoline from under the kitchen counter along with the stove lighter. She tearfully walked out, soaked the pile, and as the lighter flicked, she echoed the words:

"I'm giving all my tears to you."

Donna, along with others that were busy about their homes rushed out when the fire ignited.

Beth stood watching the flames as if she was guarding it from anyone who dared to intervene. Donna realized what was taking place, and a huge grin spread across her face as she told the small crowd to go back to whatever it was they were doing. She walked over to Beth, hugged her and whispered...

"Long time coming."

They stood there watching the flames engulf everything and anxiously awaited Dan's return.

Questions:

1. Should Beth be seen as a complete maniac for destroying Dan's property?

2. Should she have placed her hurt aside and acted as if nothing happened, hoping that Dan would eventually regret how he treated her?

3. Should she have walked away and allowed him to go his way?

4. Can we tell who was at fault in this situation, Dan
   and/or   Beth?

4.

Code of Ethics: Games in the Workplace

She was a thirty-six -year old filing clerk; He was a 45-year old director. She needed to find her place of comfort in life; he wanted to share his life's comfort with someone less fortunate and who would be able to help him rekindle feelings he had not experienced for a long time.

Her name was Alesha and she was desperately searching for her break in life. Alesha often compared herself to other females who seemed to have progressive and fulfilled lives.

She had started her new job as a filing clerk which she found through an employment agency. She was the eldest of her co-workers but was often praised for her youthful appearance. Often mistaken for a teenager, fresh out of high school, she would always worry that this might create problems for her in the workplace. She believed this could be a blessing or a curse.

She recalled on the day of her interview, how her now employers joked about how she would be the envy of her fellow coworkers. She recalled glancing across the table only to see that one of the interviewers, Ms. Beckford, sported a frown on her face each time the others complimented her.

Nevertheless, Alesha gracefully accepted the compliments and made every effort to make a good impression in the interview, at which she succeeded, because she landed the job.

Despite feeling threatened by Ms. Beckford, who was now her supervisor, Alesha knew she had to find a way to become an asset to the company. When she finally settled in her position, she diligently attempted every task given to her, even those that were not included in her job description. Alesha quickly proved her dedication and competence by completing her tasks promptly. However, Ms. Beckford would still somehow find something to complain about and took every chance she got to remind Alesha that she was her superior and was in a higher league at all times.

The company made its mark as a leading distribution establishment owned by the two brothers, Anthony and Daniel Black. They were often addressed by the initial of their first name, along with their Surname. Mr. A. Black was the one to oversee the operation of the accounting aspect, while Mr. D. Black paid more attention to the manufacturing aspect. It is said that they grew up in a very poor community and knew the ugly truths about poverty. They often spoke of their journey and how their experience would always be a reminder to help the less fortunate. Based on their beliefs, Alesha believed she would be given the chance to prove her dedication to the job.

Alesha worked alongside seven other females, three of whom came on board the same time she did. Others already employed there, boasted about the close relationship they had with the brothers, and even seemed to play a part in some of the decisions made daily. It was clear that the behavior of some of the employees could be linked to something that had plagued the world of work for centuries—the monster known as "office politics."

Alesha knew that no matter how hard she worked or tried to make an impression on her superiors, she would never be able to compete with the existing females. They prized themselves in the way they dressed and the lengthy hairpieces they paraded around the office. Besides the need to be in the good graces of their superiors, there was also a spot that seemed to be an attraction for the attention-seeking ladies - the Accounting Department.

It seated four employees, two of whom were males, but all of whom played an important part in the organization. The department was blessed with the quiet unprovoked presence of the Chief Accountant, Mr. Nelson, who managed to get the business on track with few or no words spoken. But it is said for every calm spirit placed on this earth, there is an opposite. This was proven by the demeanor of the second male presence in the department—John Durrant, affectionately called 'Slikk'.

He earned the nickname 'Slikk' because of the pride he took in his appearance. He was tall with dark complexion. Though nothing like a movie star, he came close with his appearance. Slikk's garments were of designer nature. Their perfect, snug fit did a lot to compliment his slender but manly figure. Being 45 years old was of no concern to him, as he made certain he competed well with all the other males contracted to the company. His choice of vehicles varied, but he primarily paraded in his beloved

Benz, which he did nothing to hide. He wanted it to be known that he did well for himself. He often bragged about the many businesses he owned, cars he rented, apartments he bought and sold and of course, his diesel delivery truck which he called his "Betsy."

Slikk used all that he was blessed with to build the life he wanted. There was much talk of his unpleasant demeanor towards workers less fortunate than himself. Many even complained that he went 'all-out' to throw this in their faces. Slikk often heard of the talks being made behind his back, but never showed he cared. It was even rumored that he was in a relationship with his Secretary, Shanique. Ms. Beckford had no control over that situation because she was just as close to the owners as Shanique was.

Slikk's response was always that he worked hard for all he had, so who cares what anyone thinks. His role as Director of Planning played a large part in that boastful behavior. He praised himself for being able to generate the right ideas to steer the company in a profitable direction. He was attractive to many, so it was no surprise when talks of him also being in a relationship with the cruel supervisor, Janice Beckford surfaced.

Ms Beckford thought of herself as the 'first lady' in the company, and to many, she had a huge effect on the decision-making process. After all, she was close to the brothers and conducted various businesses on their behalf.

She could not measure up to many others physically, but she often boasted that her education gave her the right to a leadership role, though many times, it was proven that the level of education she boasted about, was the same as anyone else's. The employees believed that she was given the right to make and break any rule she saw fit, as long as she got the job done. It was obvious that the talks of her relationship with Slikk were far beyond just gossips, as she made this noticeable with the excessive hours spent in his office, which was against company protocols and ethics, ones expected to be adhered to at any place of work.

For Ms. Beckford, this was of no concern to anyone other than her and Slikk. She made sure that the staff knew that she was his 'sidepiece'. She made certain everyone knew she had earned the right to be mad at him at any time and in anyone's presence, though he was often embarrassed by this and hesitantly spoke to her after her outbursts.

Alesha along with her co-worker, recalled one occasion when Janice ranted to Slikk about her car having mechanical issues. Her behavior was that of a teenager, angry with her high school 'crush', and although this type of behavior was not in any way appropriate for any place of work, Slikk just ignored it, and did everything he could to keep her happy.

***

"Here, Ms. Beckford. I am finished with the files you asked me to re-arrange," said Alesha.

"Let me see here... This is not what I asked you to do Alesha. You did the complete opposite of what I asked," replied Ms. Beckford.

"With all due respect Ms. Beckford, I do not know how differently this could have been done. I even made additions for them to look more presentable," said Alesha.

"That's where the problem lies. Did I ask you to make additions? Please follow the instructions you are given," replied Ms. Beckford.

"OK, Ms. Beckford, I will do so next time. Would you like me to undo the changes?"

"Please do. And Alesha, I noticed that your skirt is a bit tight. Please remember this is an office, and we must always dress professionally. Do not pay attention to anyone else's attire and remember that your dignity speaks for itself."

"Dignity, Ms. Beckford? And can you please tell me where does that statement fit in this conversation? I have done nothing that should cause my dignity to be questioned. Please ma'am, treat me with the same respect I have extended to you. And I ask you to take into consideration the fact that the company has not yet provided me with uniforms. Besides, ma'am, not everyone can afford the company's idea of a proper dress code. I certainly can't." said Alesha.

"Excuse me, should I take this as a sign that you are challenging my requests?" asked Ms. Beckford with her right eyebrow raised.

"No, Ms. Beckford, I am just making you aware of my position as it relates to my financial obligations."

"No more lip please, a little too much of that. And besides, the uniform is on the agenda, just be patient."

"Ok mam," Alesha replied.

Alesha had begun to notice that Slikk would glance at her occasionally whenever he walked past her desk, which was very rare. He, however, made sure he gave Ms. Beckford no indication that his attention was set anywhere other than on her. It was something Alesha would silently laugh at and had no idea others were doing the same. She had heard talk of him being a ladies' man, and one among the lot whose name often echoed for the reason of having relationships with multiple females in the company, so it was of no surprise to Alesha that Ms. Beckford would want to keep a close eye on Slikk's every move. She believed Ms. Beckford's attitude never placed a damper on Slikk's efforts, as he portrayed himself to be a man who went after whatever he wanted.

Alesha had heard stories of females being fired because Ms. Beckford thought Slikk was romantically interested in them. She was branded the "witch from hell," and many wondered how she had gotten away with calling herself a child of God. Many often wondered how Slikk could be involved with someone of that nature, even though he was living with a counterpart that he spoke very highly of. It was said that he had no choice but to be with Ms. Beckford, as he feared losing his job. She had a great deal of influence on the business, and on many occasions showed that whatever she says, goes.

Alesha was oftentimes unhappy while she worked, simply fighting to get through each day. She was thinking of ways to make her mark in the establishment even though she was given no credit for the work she did daily. Her meager salary did little or nothing to make her feel like a valuable employee. She once found herself teaching Ms. Beckford and her assistant Kayon how to maneuver their way around the accounting software and she also took over the role of Kayon whenever she was absent.

Other staff members would often reach out to Alesha for her assistance in finding solutions to problems that presented themselves daily. She did all that was asked even though she was never recognized by her superiors. Instead, she had to settle for the many jokes made about her age and the stares whenever she walked by. She was targeted by other females in the office, who believed that she caught the attention of too many male employees.

***

It was Friday, and the staff was permitted to dress casually. Alesha wore her well-fitted blue jeans with a yellow polo shirt and black lace-up shoes. She made sure not to deviate from the expected dress code. Somehow, she knew the moment she walked in that morning, Ms. Beckford was going to find something wrong with her attire, especially because of the compliments she received while on her way up to the office. She could feel the sensation of piercing eyes on her back as she approached her workstation, though she pretended not to notice.

"Good morning, Alesha."

She looked up to find Ms. Beckford standing over her with a puzzled expression on her face.

"Morning, Ms. Beckford," Alesha replied.

"Did you read the manual for how one should be attired on a Friday?"

"Ms. Beckford, is there something wrong with what I am wearing? Isn't it Friday? Am I not wearing jeans and polo?" Alesha asked.

"Please, do not let me have to take this up with Mr. A. Black. On several occasions, I spoke to you about wearing tight clothing. Not only are your pants too tight, but it also carries a pattern. I also made it clear that laced shoes are not allowed."

"What pattern, Ms. Beckford? Some parts are just a bit darker than the rest, and no ma'am, I do not recall any memo about shoes with laces."

Ms. Beckford was not at all amused by Alesha's defense. She rolled her eyes and faintly stomped her feet, as a sign of her patience running low.

Alesha turned to see that all eyes were now on her.

"Young lady," Ms. Beckford continued, "It appears we are going to have to continue this conversation in my office since you are having a hard time following my rules."

As Alesha walked behind her, she was surprised by a male's voice.

"Don't you look nice today." Alesha.

She turned to see that the compliment was coming from Mr. A. Black, who was just entering the office.

"Thank you, sir," Alesha replied softly.

"I do not believe you are complimenting her on the very thing I am about to reprimand her. Mr. Black, there are rules set in this company, ones that must be followed or everyone will think they can do whatever they wish." ranted Ms. Beckford.

"Good Morning to you, Ms. Beckford. I honestly do not see anything wrong with Alesha's attire. But, as you said, rules implemented must be followed, and I assume you know best."

Mr. Black chuckled as he made his way to his office.

Alesha entered Ms. Beckford's office, and was reprimanded. Ms. Beckford reminded her of the status she held in the company. She also made it clear that at no point will she be disrespected, including being talked back to by any member of staff. Alesha could not help but notice that as she spoke, her eyes ran up and down her body. She went on, telling Alesha that she must take into consideration that the office includes male employees, whose minds will be easily distracted from their duties.

"How am I distracting anyone from doing their job, Ms. Beckford?" asked Alesha.

"I didn't say you were. I am letting you know not to do anything to start. Besides, have you seen the way you dress?"

"Ms. Beckford, I am truly confused. I dress like all the other ladies in the office, I have no control over how my outfits compliment my curves." Alesha replied.

"Young lady, never compare yourself with anyone. And please keep in mind you are new here."

Alesha had many issues she needed to be addressed. She wanted to tell Ms. Beckford about how unfair she was being treated and how sad she felt about not getting recognition for her efforts. She wanted to shout that she was a victim of undeserved scrutiny, but she knew her words would be in vain. She also knew that Ms. Beckford had nothing but envy for her, so she chose to agree with all that was said, vowing to keep in line with the "laws of the land."

"Now that you understand where we stand, I do not expect us to have a repeat of this conversation going forward."

"We won't Ms. Beckford," Alesha replied.

As Alesha left, she was just in time to see Kayon coming in, attired similarly as herself. She wore bright orange jeans, complemented by matching shoes.

Alesha looked back to make sure Ms. Beckford was right behind her.

"Good morning Ms. Beckford," said Kayon.

"Good morning, my dear. I like those heels. You must tell me where you bought them."

Alesha stared at Ms. Beckford. She realized she was being taunted by the compliments given to Kayon. She returned to her seat and sat for a few moments in disbelief before beginning her daily tasks. She was soon interrupted by another member of staff who came over to her.

"Take it easy, girl. Trust me, you will not be the first nor the last to be targeted by the Witch. Do your work as expected and keep your head up. She has done this to others, and girl, you are going to come under attack because you look really great."

Alesha smiled. Every word said was the truth, but no one she worked with could be trusted, as they were caught on many occasions giving her the same look as Ms. Beckford. Alesha spent the rest of her day wrapped up in her work and quietly went about her business. She was soon jolted back to the reality of being in the workplace, by the ringing of the office line.

"Good afternoon. How may I help you?" Alesha answered.

"Alesha, can you come to my office please?"

Though she recognized the voice, she was still surprised that Mr. Durrant was the one calling her. Their only previous exchange of words were merely salutations.

"Yes, sir, I will be there," Alesha replied.

As she got up from her desk, she looked to see if Ms. Beckford was close by. With no visible sign of her,

Alesha nervously walked towards Slikk's office, because she knew Ms. Beckford had an issue with anyone going there. She knocked on the door and entered at his invitation.

"Good afternoon, sir," Alesha said.

"Good afternoon, Alesha. How are you?" Slikk asked.

"I am well, sir."

"Are you sure about that?"

"Yes, Mr. Durrant, I am."

"I can't see how, when I was informed that you are not being treated properly."

"What do you mean sir?" Alesha asked.

"I heard that persons here are treating you as if you are beneath them. If that is the case, it needs to be addressed. This is where we all spend most of our days, so I would want to make certain that we are all working in an environment that makes us feel welcomed and at ease. I believe this is the best formula to get the work done. Wouldn't you agree, Alesha?"

"Yes Mr. Durrant, I would, but I am fine. I will cope with the surroundings and those I have to work with."

"Well, that sounds like you are definitely having an issue. Let me know now, so I can sort it out when I meet with the rest of the directors," he replied.

"Thank you, sir, but there is nothing to sort out."

Alesha wondered how he came to this assumption, even though she wanted so much to tell him it was not a rumor. She knew that even if she admitted it was true, there would not be much he would be able to do. No one did anything to help the others before her who faced the same ordeal.

"Is that all, sir?" Alesha asked.

"Yes, for that aspect. How old are you Alesha?"

"I am thirty-six, sir."

"What? Thirty-six?"

"Yes, sir."

"You look much younger."

"Thank you Sir."

Just as before, Alesha became very fearful of such a compliment.

"You are welcome. If I might add, you are looking lovely today," Slikk said.

As she was about to leave the office, she noticed that Slikk was now laid back in his chair, watching her as she walked out.

"OK, sir. Thank you," said Alesha.

"Please do not be afraid to visit sometime."

Alesha knew it was time to go, as she could hear her co-workers' footsteps trampling down the stairs. She hurriedly returned to her desk to retrieve her bag and was greeted by Ms. Beckford's unwelcomed voice.

"Well, you were missing for quite some time. Where were you?"

With a passive expression, Alesha replied, "In the Director's office."

"I see. Have a good weekend now," said Ms. Beckford.

"Thank you, and you as well ma'am," replied Alesha.

She walked towards the exit, but stopped and turned to see Ms. Beckford heading towards Mr. Durrant's office. She giggled as she thought about the hell that was going to take place inside.

"What a weekend he will have," whispered Alesha, as she left for home.

***

It was now Sunday. As Alesha got up out of bed and threw the meat in the sink, she was bothered by how fast the weekend went. For her, the thought of seeing Ms. Beckford's face tomorrow made today seem like her last day of peace. Her phone rang and interrupted her thoughts. She rushed from the kitchen to take the call.

"Hi. Good morning," she answered.

"Hi, Alesha."

"Mr. Durrant?" she asked.

"Yes, and you can call me Slikk today. We are not at work."

"How may I help you, on a Sunday? And I would ask how you got my number, but we both know you have access to all files."

"You are quite clever" he chuckled.

"I'm sorry sir. I am just not used to speaking with anyone from work on a Sunday," Alesha expressed.

"I understand. Well, I was on my way to the country, and I opted to take this route. Unfortunately, my vehicle suddenly stopped working right here on Greenwich

Avenue. I am not familiar with this area, and I guess panic triggered the memory of you mentioning you live nearby. I called for help from a friend who works with a security company, but I do not know how long that will take. I just wondered how close by you were, and if you could come to keep me company until they arrive?"

"Where exactly are you, sir?"

Alesha realized Slikk was at the top of her street. She was uncomfortable with keeping a man company for all eyes in the community to see, but she believed he needed her, so she hesitantly replied,

"Ok, Sir, I'm coming."

"Thank you. I'll be right here waiting," Slikk replied.

Alesha got dressed and went to meet him. As she walked toward the top of her street, she saw his Benz parked alongside the road. It seemed strange that the vehicle was perfectly parked on the opposite side of the road. Nevertheless, she made no mention of her thoughts.

"Hi, sir. Are you OK?" Alesha asked.

"Yes, much better now. Wow, don't you look good in shorts."

Alesha slowly moved away from the door of his vehicle, as if being on the alert.

"That was meant as a compliment, not something to scare you," he replied.

"I am not scared, but very cautious."

"I do understand. And you can call me Slikk. We are not at work."

"Ok, Sir, I mean Slikk."

"That's much better," he said.

He invited her to sit in his car until help arrived, but she declined. She was worried about being too close to him.

They began talking, and Alesha started to feel a bit more relaxed in his company. She started to believe he was not as bad as others made him out to be. He told her she was an attractive young lady. She told him that he was a slick individual, for whom she had great respect. They talked for a while with no mention of anything work-related.

She now remembered her meat in the sink, but she thought to help Slikk in his time of trouble was of far more importance.

"Can I invite you out sometime?" he asked. "Can I help you to find what you are looking for?" Slikk asked.

"Who told you I was looking for something?"

"I have been around for some time. I have seen and done it all. I know when someone needs direction, and I know you need that right now."

"Sir, I have been through quite a lot in my life, and life has not been kind to me. I have given so many chances to those who didn't deserve any at all. So, for me, being alone is my best option now," said Alesha.

"I understand, but please remember not every man will hurt you. Let's start with friendship for now, and allow the rest to find its way in," Slikk continued.

Alesha looked at him and wondered if these were just words coming from another player's mouth. He told her he wanted to be there for her in every way possible, and that he had more than enough to share. She took comfort in his words, but she knew she needed time to put real meaning to what he had said. So, with a slight smile, she replied, "OK sir, I'll think about it".

"Alesha, you will not regret saying yes," said Slikk.

"I didn't say yes. I said I'll think about it."

They were interrupted by the sound of bike engines coming in their direction.

They are here," Slikk uttered.

Men on motorcycles stopped alongside his vehicle. They were dressed in armored uniforms as if contracted to a security company. Slikk told her they were the ones he was awaiting.

"Good morning young lady. You might make a good team member, as you did a good job of keeping my friend safe," replied one of the guards.

Alesha smiled at the compliment. She could tell by the way he conversed with Slikk, that they were good friends.

"Well Slikk, I have to leave now," said Alesha.

"Why so soon?" he asked.

"I have dinner to prepare, and now that your friends are here to take over, I know you are safe."

"Fair enough; thanks for your company. See you on Monday."

"Take care, Sir." And with that, she headed towards home.

She battled for the rest of the day with all that Slikk had said to her. She had prayed so hard for help with her financial woes, she knew now his offer came just at the right time. She also knew she did not want any relationship, other than friendship with another male, especially not with Slikk. After all, everyone knew he was Ms. Beckford's property.

***

Weeks passed, and even though they were no less stressful, Alesha tried hard to find her answer to Slikk's request, while trying to ignore his glances that had become stares, ones he gave every time he walked past her desk. She noticed that Ms. Beckford had been spending more time in his office, and on more than one occasion, would storm out in anger. Alesha felt guilty about enjoying that they weren't getting along, but she felt relieved that Ms. Beckford did not have the time to make her the centre of any further attention. It was as if she had forgotten that she even existed.

Alesha's thoughts were interrupted by the ringing of the office line

"Good day. How may I help you?" she answered.

"Alesha, can you come to my office, please?"

"I'm coming, Sir," she replied.

She walked faintly towards his doors. Her hand shook as she knocked.

"Come in," he said, "Can you please sit?"

"I'll stand, Sir," Alesha replied.

"Young lady, please sit," he demanded.

His tone pressured her into doing exactly what was asked. She was nervous about being there and so she looked uneasy as she sat in the chair.

"When you are called to my office, I expect you to be calm and relaxed. You are in a professional setting, so there is no need for you to feel uncomfortable."

"Yes, Sir," replied Alesha.

With a grin on his face and no hesitation whatsoever, Slikk asked if she had thought about his proposal. Although she was expecting this moment, it still came as a surprise to her that he would be expecting an answer so soon.

"Yes, I have, but I am yet to make a decision."

"I understand. While you are still thinking, can I invite you out for drinks this Friday?"

"Me, Mr. Durrant? Drinks…this Friday?"

"Yes, you —is there someone else here?"

"Where will we be going, Sir? I must tell you I am not comfortable with anyone seeing us out together. I am scared they will get the wrong idea."

"Well, Alesha, the only idea they should get is us having drinks together. Maybe you don't realize, but that is what I am inviting you to do. Why are you so shy? I watch you from time to time on the security cameras, and it is as if you are afraid to even talk with anyone."

"I am, sir. But right now, I am more concerned."

A Code of Ethics: Games in the Workplace

"There is nothing to be concerned about. You will be with me, and trust me, there is no safer place to be."

With a huge sigh, she uttered, "OK, sir, I'll come."

Slikk's face lit up, "Where should I pick you up?"

"I will let you know."

"Thank you, Alesha. You will not regret this. Now, go and do your work, and please, allow no one to steal your joy for the rest of the day."

"I'll try sir," Alesha replied.

She returned to her desk and continued her day's activities. Thankfully, she managed to avoid Ms. Beckford for the rest of the week.

***

It was the end of another week, and Alesha tried not to think about seeing Slikk. She gathered her things and clicked the shutdown button on her computer. Before she could head towards the door, she was halted by a text message on her phone.

It read, *"I can't wait to see you later."*

Alesha smiled making certain she was looking right at the office camera. She was sure she was being watched, as Slikk told her he did on many occasions.

Now nightfall, her cell phone rang.

"Hello," Alesha answered.

"Hi, are you ready?" Slikk replied.

"Yes, I am."

"Where are you?" he asked.

"I am at the stop below where your vehicle broke down."

"OK, I'm coming."

She waited nervously for his arrival and prayed that no one she knew would see her getting in his vehicle. As he pulled up, she opened the door and quickly slid into the front passenger seat. For a short while, there was silence on both sides.

"Hi, sir," she finally uttered.

"You look great Alesha, so different from the way you look at work. I hardly recognized you."

He stared at her as if he was seeing her for the first time. She smiled because she was convinced her efforts had paid off. She wanted to make a lasting impression on him, so she took time and effort to put herself together. Although she was never one for the whole works of makeup, tonight she made an exception. With her hair let down and her above the knee dress, she made it hard for Slikk to keep his eyes anywhere other than on her.

"Where are we going?" Alesha asked.

"Not far from here, you'll see," Slikk replied.

Their short journey had very little conversation, as Slikk seemed caught up with the appearance of the lady in the front seat of his Benz.

"We're here," he finally said.

Though their destination was close by, Alesha did not recognize it.

Slikk was met by two guards who opened the well-secured gate of the establishment. As they entered, Alesha recognized one of the guards as Slikk's friend, who had come to his rescue in his time of trouble. Slikk smiled at her. They got out of the car and were immediately greeted by him

"Good evening," he said. "We meet again under more relaxed circumstances. You look lovely tonight."

"Thank you," she answered, "Don't you look the same."

They all laughed, as he was once again dressed in his uniform.

Slikk took her and led her to the tower of the building. Awaiting them was a table not yet set, except for the two chairs placed there.

Alesha did not give much thought to this. She was more taken up with the beautiful view from the rooftop and the sensational tunes that brought tranquility to the night.

"Are you OK, my dear?" Slikk asked.

"Yes, I am," she replied.

"Have you realized that the table is not set with anything in particular?"

"It's not? Did not see that," she laughed.

"I told them to leave it empty because I want tonight to be all about getting to know you; your likes and dislikes, what makes you happy or sad. I want you to make your choices for tonight, and that will help me to know your choices for the future. So, your first task for the night is to choose your drink."

Alesha was flattered by all Slikk had said. For the first time in her life, someone cared enough to allow her to choose, even if it was just a choice of drink.

"Rum and coke," she said. She knew the occasion called for Champagne, but she would not enjoy such glamour. She chose what she drank when hanging with her girls, mostly because that's all they could afford.

"Rum and coke it is," Slikk replied.

He politely opted for Appleton laced with red bull. He signaled to his friend that they were ready to order.

"Has the lady decided?" his friend asked.

"Yes, rum and coke for her, and the usual for me."

Alesha realized the depth of their friendship; 'the usual' meant they met on many occasions to drink and chat. She now believed they somewhat supported each other's decisions, and in that instant, she felt scared.

"The usual? So, you two are brothers from another mother?" Alesha asked inquisitively.

"You can say that. I have known Caine for many years, we have been through a lot together, and we supported each other for most of our lives. We do not always agree with each other's actions, but we always have each other's back.

"Oh my, Alesha, I've just realized, you two were not officially introduced."

The conversation was interrupted by the delivery of their drinks.

"Here you go, ma'am; one rum and coke, and for you Sir, a flask of Appleton, two Red Bulls, and of course, your bucket of ice."

As Caine placed the items on the table, he smiled at Alesha and patted Slikk on the shoulder.

"Wait a minute Caine, I am officially introducing you to this lovely lady here,' said Slikk.

"Caine, this is Alesha, my beautiful lady for the night, and Alesha this is Caine, my good friend." They both shook hands. As Caine left the table, Alesha felt she had to ask Slikk about the gesture Caine made.

"So, what was that pat for?" she asked.

"Truth be told, he was just acknowledging how gorgeous you are looking."

"All this seem like something you have both experienced before," said Alesha.

"If you are asking me if I have taken anyone else here, the answer is 'no."

"I was not asking that. That would not be any of my business," Alesha replied.

"Of course, it would. What you do from now on will matter to me, and I would expect that it will be the same for you." Slikk said.

For Alesha, Slikk's words meant he wanted her to become a part of his life. But she was not yet sure this was something she was ready to accept.

It seemed that they had talked the night away. Slikk proved to be a heavy drinker, as Caine returned numerous times to replace his order and mocked Alesha for barely touching hers. Though she was not new to drinking her favorite mixture, she knew she could become easily lightheaded after even the first sip. As a result, she did what she knew would keep her sober.

"Are you sure you will be sober enough to drive us both home?" she asked.

"Oh please, Alesha! I am just having a few drinks of water; Caine can vouch for me. It would take a ton load of this stuff to even get me tipsy. I have been doing this since my teenage years, so my system has gotten used to it by now," Slikk boasted.

"OK Slikk, I hear you," replied Alesha.

"Finally! You called me Slikk. Now, I know you are comfortable being around me. That's was my intent."

"Yes, I do feel more relaxed, enough to ask you about your relationship with Ms. Beckford."

"What relationship?" Slikk replied.

"You tell me. It is very obvious you two are seeing each other," said Alesha.

With a laugh, Slikk declared, "Yes we are. We see each other every day at work."

"Time for truth. Please do not lie to me." Alesha probed.

"I am not lying. The relationship Ms. Beckford and I have is not as everyone thinks. She and I were both with the company since the beginning. We work together, we both make many decisions together, and yes, we were once involved, but not anymore." Slikk said.

"You do know that she does not see things that way, right?" Alesha said.

"Yes, I do, but she and I both know the truth."

"So, is there a Mrs. Durrant?" Alesha asked.

"No, I am not married, but I do live with someone, and she means a lot to me."

"Well, if she does, what are you doing here?"

Slikk fumbled to find a response. "It's complicated, Alesha. I love her, and we respect each other, but I do not know if that is the life I want. I guess that was one of the things that led to my involvement with Janice, and I can truly say I regret that choice now."

"But there is so much talk about you being involved with females other than her," Alesha pressed. "Are you involved with Shanique?"

"My secretary? What! Do not tell me that is one of the talks?" asked Slikk.

"Yes, it is. Is it true?"

"No, it's not," said Slikk.

"Shanique came to work with me when she was young. I hired her as a favor to a friend. We bonded because at that time she lost her dad, and I guess she saw me as someone who could replace him. We became close because I look out for her just as a dad would. So of course, it's only natural that she would cling to me, and she even gets jealous at times, just as a daughter would feel about her father."

Alesha felt a bit of pity for Slikk. She concluded that some of the talks about him were not true. She also saw that he was trying hard to bury his regrets in his drinking.

"Ok, I understand," said Alesha.

"So, what about you? What's your story?" Slikk asked.

"No story; not much to tell. As I told you before, I am still trying to find my prince in life, and it does not help that so many 'frogs' are lined up to be 'kissed."

Slikk laughed. "Are you calling me a frog?"

"I guess I am. So many males have tried to convince me that they are the one to change my life. My life has already been changed by my daughter who means everything to me. And besides, their talks have all just been empty promises."

"Oh, you have a daughter?" asked Slikk.

"Yes, she's a teenager. She's not living with me right now because I am trying to get my life on track, but everything I try to accomplish, I do it with her in mind.

"I understand very well. I have a daughter as well, and even though she is living overseas, my whole life revolves around her. I would not replace her for anything or anyone in this world; she's my life," Slikk paused for a moment.

"Alesha I really like you; can we be more than friends?" he asked.

"Slikk, to tell you the truth, it seems that all the females in the company are involved with someone there. I do not want to be a part of that cycle. This is all just happening too fast for me. I do not want to be branded with everyone else in the office. I do not want to lose my job over this, but most of all; I do not want my heart to be broken again. I have experienced what that feels like, and I will never go back to that place. Never."

"You will not—not with me. I want you to trust me," he assured her.

He rose from his seat and took her by the hand. He stood with his back pressed against the railing that made the perfect spot for the view from the rooftop. He laid her head in his chest and gently kissed her forehead. The cold fresh air that brought life to the night gave her the chills, so she applied pressure to his chest. He knew that was an invitation for his arms to give her warmth, so he wrapped them tightly around her and rested his head on hers. As she closed her eyes, she knew this moment would play an essential role in her letting him in her life.

***

As time passed, Alesha's nights now became occupied with Slikk's numerous calls and texts. He bought her a phone that would ensure he got through to her at all times, as the one she had was not up to his standard. They were now enjoying each other's company on many occasions. Slikk made sure his weekends revolved solely around her. She became accustomed to his presence.

He now began having an issue with her taking public transportation or accepting a ride from anyone other than himself, so he opted to give her a personal chauffeur, who was no other than Caine. He was supposed to take her wherever she had an appointment and whenever he was unable to make it, a taxi would be called.

With her concern for her job and Slikk's concern for her happiness, they both did everything they could to hide their involvement from everyone. In public, they passed each other as if only co-workers. She stayed away from his office and only went there when she was summoned by him. Even this proved a challenge, as he used every chance, he got to show her how much he missed her company. He often told her that she needed to come to pick up forms to take back to her supervisor, but when she did, she instead had his chest pressed up against her bosom and his lips pasted on hers.

Alesha found herself being jealous of other females entering his office, even though he had assured her that his involvement with them was merely platonic and professional. She often saw Shanique sitting with him as if she was just making conversations. Talks of their potential involvement always flashed across Alesha's mind, but she tried to remember what Slikk explained to her, so she opted to take comfort in his words.

While Ms. Beckford was still somewhat angry about the situation between herself and Slikk, she would occasionally go by his office then emerge with netted brows. Alesha seemed to have somehow found a way to pay no attention to her and her shenanigans, which caused her job to be much easier.

The Directors often joked about Slikk, and how they could tell his Friday nights were being spent a bit differently and that he and Ms. Beckford were not getting along. They believed that she was trying hard to make him regret ever getting mad at her, as her jeans became more tightly fitted and her hairpieces longer. She made certain her makeup was "spot on" or so she believed because she was often secretly laughed at for the way her garments did nothing to compliment her figure and her makeup which often made her look like a clown. After all, she was not one to watch what she ate, and didn't care about the fact that the rules she put in place for everyone else to follow did not apply to her, but no one dared to comment on any of it. After all, she was the 'first lady'.

As for Alesha, things were finally looking up. Slikk may just be keeping his promise.

Her work line rang.

"Hi, good day. How may I help you?" said Alesha.

"Can you come to my office please," replied Slikk.

"Yes Sir."

With a smile on her face, she got up from her chair. As she passed Shanique's door, she noticed she was staring at her, as a daughter disapproving of her father's mistress. Alesha quickly dismissed her actions and knocked on Slikk's door.

"Come," said Slikk.

"Yes Sir, you called," replied Alesha.

"Have a seat please, ma'am. How are you today, Alesha?"

"I am good, Sir"

"Are you sure?"

"Yes. I am."

"Let me get straight to the reason I called you here-" Before he could continue, he was interrupted by a knock on the door.

"Come," he said.

"Hi, Sir."

"Hi, Shanique. How may I help you?"

"Well, Sir, I was just wondering if you still wanted the files you asked me for?"

"Files? Oh yes, of course, I do. But I am not yet ready for them. I will call you when I am."

"Ok, Sir," replied Shanique.

Alesha began wondering if Shanique's visit was for any reason other than the one she gave. Nonetheless, she brushed her thoughts aside. She knew his secretary is expected to visit his office regularly since she was the one working closest to him. Shanique finally left the office though somewhat hesitant.

So, Alesha, where were we?" asked Slikk.

"I don't recall, sir," replied Alesha.

"Oh yes. I called you here because I was looking at my camera sometime earlier this week, and I saw the young man who works in the factory standing over you at your desk. It was clear that you were both in deep conversation. Is there something I should know about?"

"Young man, sir? I do not recall." Said Alesha.

"Really? I am talking about Scott. Do you recall now?" asked Slikk.

"Yes, I do. He wanted to know if he could purchase an item on credit. I told him I was not the correct person to speak to. Is there something wrong, sir?" asked Alesha.

"Yes, there is. I do not feel comfortable seeing any males here—or anywhere for that matter—indulging in such deep talks with you. If I haven't told you before, let me say it now, I am very jealous. It matters to me whom you converse with, even if it is about the job."

Alesha sighed, rolled her eyes in frustration, and thought about how his words came across as ultimatums. She tried to differentiate between her conversations with coworkers and his conversations with those who visited his office.

Slikk leaned back in his chair. His no-nonsense look immediately got her attention. They both stared at each other for a moment, before he said. "You belong to me and no one else. Are we clear?"

In a low tone, she responded, "Yes, we are."

"Since that is now out of the way, can I see you tonight?" he asked.

"Tonight, Sir? No, tonight will not be good for me," replied Alesha.

"Why not?"

"Because, I have things to sort out at home."

"It's a Wednesday. What about sorting them out tomorrow?"

"No, Sir, I can't. They are of priority."

"I understand. So, when can I see you?" he asked.

"I guess Saturday will be good," Alesha replied.

"Saturday. What about tomorrow or Friday?"

"Sir, as I told you before, I have obligations. I will not be available before Saturday."

"OK. I guess I will just have to wait until then." Slikk mumbled.

"I guess so," Alesha concluded.

As she rose to leave, he asked her to sit.

"Why the hurry? What do you have to do that is so important you want to rush from my office?"

"The company's work, Sir, I would see that as a priority."

"Aren't you a lady of words," he laughed. "OK, go do your company's work, but before you leave, I want you to have this."

He took an envelope hidden under a pile of papers on his desk and handed it to her.

"Do not open it until you get home."

"Is this money?" she asked. "What is it for?"

"Yes, it is. And it's for you to do whatever you please, but please follow my instructions and open it when you get home," replied Slikk.

"Ok, I will. Thank you," she said.

"I told you I am going to take care of you, so my dear have yourself a great day."

She placed the envelope in a pile of notes she had taken to his office, which always seemed to be her cover for going there. She returned to her seat to find Ms. Beckford, with arms folded, standing alongside the column behind her desk, as if awaiting her return.

"Have you completed the filing that has accumulated since last week?" asked Ms. Beckford.

"They are not accumulating, ma'am, as I explained to you. I was having an issue with finding where to place them because they were much disorganized, but I have used my initiative in getting them somewhat together. So, when I am through, it should be much easier to locate them. So yes, I have completed the job since last Friday," said Alesha.

"Initiative? Is that the word used instead of the phrase 'do as you please'? Why didn't you wait on me to give you directives as to how exactly I wanted you to proceed? Do you know that the directors use those files at times? The files need to be kept updated as well as organized. I do hope the fact that you keep leaving your desk so often is not interfering with the quality of work you are expected to deliver."

"Ms. Beckford, with all due respect ma'am, if I were to come to you every time, I have an issue with filing papers, then you would not need me for the job at all. I do not believe I was hired to only do what is asked of me, but to also use my initiative to correct problems without having to run to my supervisor, who I am sure is occupied with more important issues. And ma'am, I do not leave my desk for any reason other than that associated with the job. So I do not find your statement at all true." Alesha defended herself confidently.

"Well, all I am asking is that you do your job the way it is supposed to be done, and then go home," said Ms. Beckford.

Ms. Beckford walked away, and Alesha noticed that everyone had stopped what they were doing to eavesdrop on what was being said. Ms. Beckford had taken no care to make their discussion a secret. Alesha knew that Slikk was watching on his camera because he shortly walked by her desk and glanced at her as if to see if she was upset about what had just transpired.

Alesha smiled. She was accustomed to the many complaints from the Witch from hell, about the nature of work that she was producing. She also knew that Ms. Beckford was finding ways to play out what was happening between her and Slikk on any employee she saw fit, and for now, Alesha was the chosen one.

Alesha got through the rest of the day, by pretending no one else existed around her. It was now the best time of everyone's day. Staff rushed down the steps. For many, this was the only time they got to escape the Witch's wrath, so nobody dared to linger. Before Alesha exited the building, she looked up at Slikk's office window to see him standing, looking down at her. He had told her this was something he oftentimes did, as he admired the way she walked. She was now convinced that was true, as she witnessed his stare for herself.

"Home at last!" Alesha muttered as dropped her bags on the floor and laid on the bed, relieved to be out of Ms. Beckford's presence. She rested for a bit, then recalled that Slikk had handed her an envelope earlier and she was exactly where he instructed her to be when she opened it. She quickly got up, took it from her bag and opened it. She began to count and was astonished to see that Slikk had given her J$45,000. She knew exactly what she wanted to do with it, but she still believed she needed to know the real reason he gave her that amount. She took her phone from her bag and dialed his number, knowing that he would still be in his office after everyone else had left, as he usually was.

His phone rang.

"Hi, my dear," Slikk answered.

"I see you were expecting my call," said Alesha.

"I was anticipating it. Did you get home OK?"

"Yes, I did."

"Have you opened your package?"

"Yes. What is it for?"

"As I have said before. It's for whatever you want it to be. I want you to be taken care of, so I will have a package for you every week. No matter what happens, you must come for your package. I never want you to be in need of anything. More importantly, I never want you to ask anyone but myself for anything. Is that clear?"

"Yes, very. Thank you," Alesha replied.

"All I want you to do is to keep sweet for me."

"I will," said Alesha.

They talked for a while until he decided it was time for him to leave the office, as the evening flow of traffic would have become more manageable. Before hanging up, he told her that he thought about her a lot, and he never wanted her to leave his life because she had made an impact on his whole being. As he told her good night and hung up the phone, she could not fight the tears rolling down her face. His words were what she had longed to hear, but she was frightened of her heart being broken all over again. Her feelings for him had now gone beyond the envelope he handed her. She truly believed she had fallen.

***

"Hello," Alesha answered.

"Hi, my dear," replied Slikk.

"I'm just calling to remind you it's Saturday."

"This is new, seeing that I have never forgotten the days of the week."

"I know. Truth is I just wanted to ensure you remember we are seeing each other this evening."

"I remember, and I am looking forward to seeing you. Where are we going?"

"I would like to take you for something to eat, then we can just spend some quality time, that's if that's ok with you?" asked Slikk.

"That is fine," replied Alesha.

"I will ask Caine to pick you up. Is six good for you, at the same spot?"

"Yes, that's good."

"Can't wait to see you."

"Me neither."

Alesha took the time to make sure all was being done at home because she did not want anything on her mind for her night out with Slikk, other than him of course. She knew the time spent with him did not see everything going as planned; his idea of having a good time had no limitations. Her choice of outfit was tight fitted jeans, which she saw going very nicely with ankle-high boots. She wore a midriff top designed to show all aspects of her back. Her hair was done in a ponytail, and her accessories fit her choice of outfit.

As she walked along the path where Caine would pick her up, she was flooded with compliments of how attractive she looked. She knew Slikk would have compliments of his own, and that was something she anticipated. She waited a bit before Caine arrived.

"Wow, don't you look lovely. Wait until Slikk sees you."

She smiled as she remembered having those same thoughts. As they headed for the destination, Caine again told her that she was a very attractive young lady. He shared how often Slikk talked about her, and how overwhelmed he was to have her in his life. For a while, she thought Caine was just putting in a few good words for his friend, but she soon felt confident, realizing he was using words that Slikk had already expressed to her. She found this as an ice breaker to find out from Caine if he was acquainted with Slikk's 'thought ruler', Ms. Beckford.

He had given Alesha the impression that even though he was Slikk's wingman, he would not hold back what he knew, and so Alesha's used that to her advantage. Her efforts paid off. Caine told her that they all were associated with each other for several years. Ms. Beckford was introduced to him by Slikk, just as Alesha was, and he even mentioned how deep their relationship was.

She realized that Caine felt somewhat obligated to Ms. Beckford, as he mentioned the help she gave him on so many occasions. But even though he respected her, he was not amused by the way she manipulated Slikk, and Caine never understood why he allowed her to do so, as he knew Slikk was never one to accept anything less than respect from anyone. Caine explained how Slikk had no control over what he did when it came to dealing with Ms. Beckford.

Alesha began wondering if Slikk had told her the whole truth about his relationship with Ms. Beckford.

They had now finally reached the destination, and Alesha could see Slikk's Benz in the parking lot of the establishment. She knew that he enjoyed the setting of being out in the open because once more, they were at a restaurant solely centered around that. Caine escorted her to the table where Slikk was waiting. As she walked towards him, he stood with a look in his eyes, as if he did not recognize who was walking towards him.

"Again, you never cease to amaze me," said Slikk.

"I assume that's French for how good I look," Alesha said.

"You do look good Alesha; you are very sexy. Your work attire is doing you no justice whatsoever." She laughed as she sat down with him.

"Caine will be with us. Is that ok with you?" asked Slikk.

"Of course, it is," she said. Even though her true thought was that with three at the table, it might be a bit awkward. She then saw that he would be sitting at a table all by himself. Suddenly her concerns became worries.

"Will he be alright dining alone?" asked Alesha.

"Who, Caine? I bet he was really looking forward to that." Slikk laughed."

The waiter then walked over with the beverages. Alesha smiled as she saw that Slikk had ordered for her, making sure her drink was the same as before. He also took the liberty of ordering a variety of other beverages, just in case she wanted to try something new. Before she could begin drinking, a second waiter came with a trolley of finger foods and she thought about how well Slikk must 'cared' for his stomach.

"Will there be anything else Sir?" the waiter asked.

"I think we have enough for now," answered Slikk.

Alesha glanced over at Cain's table and saw that he was also being served, which told her that Slikk had this all planned out.

"This is a lot; are we expecting more guests?" Alesha joked.

"This is your night. I want you to feel comfortable, so I wanted you to have a lot to choose from."

"Well, I certainly do," she replied.

Slikk encouraged her to eat a bit before drinking, as that was one of the many ways to stay sober. His eyes were fixed on her as if he was in a trance.

"You are very sexy. I have never met anyone like you, and your personality is so relaxing." He was not short on issuing compliments.

"Slikk, are you involved with Ms. Beckford?"

"Hun, I thought we'd already been through that. Do I need to explain again?"

"You told me, but I need to know you are being honest with me. The last thing I want is to get involved with you, if you are already involved with someone else, at work for that matter. I told myself I would never have a relationship with someone at work, especially a director. I have gone back on that promise, so I need to make sure it means something," said Alesha.

"It does, and it will. As I've told you before, Janice wants what she and I share to be more, but I do not. She wants me to discontinue my relationship at home, so I can be all hers. That will never happen, but she refuses to accept that and won't leave me alone, even though I've shown her on many occasions that she means nothing to me. I have become very irritated with her behavior, but I have to be very cautious because she has threatened me about the possibility of losing my job. Look Alesha, Janice has a great deal of influence on the other directors; She has lied to them about me before, and whenever I try to defend myself, it seems as if I am the one that wronged her. I believe they are out for me.

"I don't understand. Why would you allow her to know so much about you, that she can constantly hold things over your head? If you want her to leave you alone, I do not see why you can't just make that clear to her. I am trying to understand, but it's hard," said Alesha.

"I do not want you to waste time focusing on Ms. Beckford and her senseless quest for me. I want you to pay attention to yourself and what you want from life... the life I am going to help you to build," replied Slikk.

Alesha realized that something was amiss, as Slikk's face began dazzling before her eyes. She tried to display normalcy but was overtaken by a kind of uncontrollable laughter, one she could not explain. She thought about getting up but quickly realized that was not an option.

"Alesha are you alright?" Slikk enquired.

"What? Of course, I am," she replied, with yet another outburst of laughter.

Caine immediately saw something was off and came over to their table.

"What's wrong with her?" he asked Slikk.

Slikk looked up at Cain, laughed, and said, "We were talking, and I did not notice that she was mixing her beverages a bit strong."

Caine laughed, "You mean she is drunk?"

"No, but very tipsy," replied Slikk.

Alesha heard every word but could not process any of it as their faces appeared to be spinning in front of her eyes.

"Are you going to take her home?" Caine asked.

"Yes, but not like this," answered Slikk. "I will just book a room and let her sleep it off for a while."

Slikk beckoned to the waiter to clear his bill as he hurried to leave.

"Leaving so soon?" Alesha asked.

"Yes, something unexpected came up." Replied Slikk.

The waiter now saw that something was wrong, as Alesha burst out laughing and laid her head on the table. Caine assisted in getting her up from the table. He threw her arm over his shoulder to support her steps, while Slikk stayed behind to take care of the bill.

Caine took her to the vehicle. "Alesha, are you going to be ok?" asked Caine.

"Yes," she laughed.

"Slikk is going to take you somewhere to sleep until you are feeling better. Are you OK with that?"

"Sleep... yes" replied Alesha.

"Don't worry. You are in good hands," Caine assured her.

He placed her in the back seat of Slikk's vehicle, so she could lay down for a bit. As Slikk got in, he turned to see if she was alright.

"You will be fine, my dear. I will see to that," said Slikk.

He pulled out of the establishment with Caine driving behind him. They approached their destination, which was close to the restaurant. Slikk got out and went to the front desk to make arrangements for a room. Caine stood at the vehicle's back door as if guarding Alesha. Slikk directed him to help her out. She had now somewhat gone off in a daze.

"Just how much did she have to drink?" asked Caine.

"I can't say—not a lot, but not sure about the mixture." Alesha's words were now slurred.

As they helped her up to the room, Slikk opened the door and Caine laid her on the bed.

"Thanks, man. I will watch her for a while until she feels better, and then take her home. I'll make sure she drinks plenty of water and sleeps it off," Slikk said to Caine.

"Sounds good. I am going to work, but call me if you need any further assistance," Caine replied.

"Cool," said Slikk.

Caine left and closed the door behind him.

Alesha curled up on the bed still fully dressed while Slikk sat beside her. She lifted her head and rested it in his lap.

"Don't worry, my dear. You will soon feel better," he assured her while caressing her forehead.

Alesha tried to take comfort in his words, but nothing could overshadow the pounding that was taking place inside her head. She began groaning.

"Alesha, I am just going to take off your shoes, is that ok?" asked Slikk.

"OK," she whispered.

She felt him gently lay beside her. She laughed and turned to face him. She fought hard to keep her focus and saw that he was staring at her with desire. She giggled as if amused, and with nothing else to do, she buried her face in his chest.

"Are you feeling any better?" he asked.

She moaned with a shake of her head.

"I have to get you a bit more comfy. Can I remove the rest of your clothes?" Slikk asked.

She looked at him in confusion and suddenly threw her head back, as if struggling to fight what was inside of her.

"No." She mumbled, *or so she thought.* He got up and began removing her pants, which became a struggle for them both, because of the way they tightly gripped her thighs. She tried to use her hands to tell him to stop, but he continued undressing her. As she struggled to get up, his hands gently pushed her down while caressing her breasts.

"You are so beautiful. I can't believe how old you really are."

"Stop… please," she said in a faint voice, "I'm not ready for this."

"Are you sure you want me to stop?" he asked.

Alesha felt herself slipping deeper into a daze. She now wondered if she was the victim of a spiked drink but convinced herself the man she had come to know would never do something like that to her.

His hands moved across her body; Alesha felt he was being a bit rough. As she tried to get out from under him, his lips heavily pressed against hers. He embraced her so close that she began tasting his cologne on her tongue. Slikk was now whispering in her ear words she could not understand. He was now in control, and for tonight, she was his, even if she did not want to be. Something different was happening, as the pain she suddenly felt was not the same as the one in her head. She tried calling out his name, but her strength began to leave her body. She thought that if he was making "love" to her, then she must have permitted it, so she gave up her efforts of fighting and he held her even closer, as he whispered, "You will always be mine, Alesha."

Alesha woke up to find Slikk fully dressed and curled up behind her with eyes wide as those of a lion watching his prey. Behind him on the night table, a clock read "3:00 AM."

"I can see you are feeling much better my love," he said.

"What? How long was I asleep?" asked Alesha.

"Long enough to feel better," Slikk replied.

She realized she was the only one undressed. In sudden fright, she asked him, "Why are my clothes removed?"

Slikk laughed. "Do you not remember anything?"

"Remember what? What happened?" asked Alesha.

"Alesha, we made love."

She turned her face away from his and sunk her head into the pillow, unable to look into his eyes.

"Lift your head, please. You do not know what you have done to me. Your warmth, your comfort, I have never experienced this, I can't explain. I will never let you go, Alesha. Never."

She was confused and struggled to comprehend Slikk's words. She wondered what had taken place but convinced herself that it would be better to not know. Besides, Slikk was with her the whole time, making certain she was safe.

"I have to go home Slikk. Please take me home."

"Are you sure you don't want to wait until morning?" he asked.

"No, I need to get home now. Where's Caine?"

"You really don't remember anything? Don't you remember Caine bringing you here?"

"No. I don't." Alesha replied.

"My dear, Caine left a while back."

As she got dressed and headed towards the door, Slikk pulled her back, with her back against his chest.

"You mean the world to me, girl. I do not want to lose you, not now." He exclaimed.

"OK," she replied, "But I need to leave now."
They headed out the door.

***

As the time passed, Alesha's style of dress was now a bit different, as Slikk had his idea of how he wanted her to be seen, and he made sure she had the means to do so. She would often be sent to stores to pick outfits of her choice, which was only made possible by Slikk's willingness to cover the bill. She was now required to wear heels more often, and at all times her nails had to be done.

Slikk made sure he was the one who picked out her perfumes because he wanted to make sure her fragrance lingered behind each time she left a room. She even changed the way she wore her hair; she was now wearing long straight hairpieces, same as the ones her coworkers paraded around the office in.

Alesha became the 'talk of the town' in the company; even the directors noticed how different she looked and joked that she was rising to new heights. She was always the first to be noticed by anyone who visited the company and would often be invited out. She began seeing herself as a target for other females in the office and even concluded there was a plot to get her out. She now saw that Ms. Beckford was finding common ground with Shanique, though everyone knew they were rivals. Alesha fought to keep her head down and go about her days as if she was the only one who existed.

"Good morning, Alesha."

"Good morning, Sir."

"Can I have a minute of your time, please?" asked Slikk.

She paused as she thought about the many eyes that would be on her going into his Office.

"Well, I'm waiting," Slikk replied.

"Yes, sir, I'm coming."

As she got up from her chair, she glanced to where Ms. Beckford sat; she was just in time to see that she was sitting still, eavesdropping on her conversation with Slikk.

"Ms. Beckford, I will be stepping away from my desk for a bit," Alesha said.

"Yes, ma'am," Ms. Beckford replied.

Alesha knew that she suspected her of being involved with Slikk, but she could not walk away from any of this now. As she went towards his office, she thought that Shanique was already informed—by Ms. Beckford—of her coming to see Slikk. Alesha's instinct once again proved to be true, as she saw Shanique standing with her face pressed against her office window as if awaiting her arrival.

"Hi, Shanique," Alesha exclaimed.

"Hi, Alesha. Going to see Slikk—I mean, Mr. Durrant?"

"Yes."

Alesha knocked on his door.

"Come," Slikk answered.

Alesha saw him in a relaxed mode in his office chair.

"How are you today, my dear?" he asked.

"I'm well, sir, except I'm wondering why your secretary calls you 'Slikk' at work?"

"Everyone calls me Slikk."

"Not on the job, I don't," said Alesha.

"Well Alesha everyone knows me by that name, so it is only natural that persons will get a bit confused at times."

"Whatever you say, sir.

"Please stop making much about nothing," he exclaimed.

She knitted her brows as a sign that she was not pleased with the response he had given.

"My dear, not the brows, please. You have nothing to worry about. Why can't you trust me?"

"You keep giving me reasons not to. Let's discuss this later. I'm sure this is not the reason you called me here." said Alesha.

"No. It's not." Do you remember I told you I did not want you accepting rides from anyone that works here?"

"How could I forget?" replied Alesha sarcastically.

"Getting cheeky, young lady? Anyway, I've instructed Caine to seek a vehicle for you. It will be nothing expensive, I just need to know you will not be dependent on anyone to get wherever you need to be. I have also made arrangements for him to give you driving lessons, so you need to look into getting your learner's license."

Alesha sat quietly, as she now saw that he was making good on his promises. She was overwhelmed with joy,

"I appreciate it," she replied with a broad grin.

"There is one other thing that I need you to deal with right away," Slikk said.

"What's that, Sir?" she asked.

"I need you to find a college of your choice and enroll. You need to further your studies, as I predict a bright future for you, one that I want to always be a part of. Do not concern yourself with financial woes, as I will take care of everything. I just need you to do what you are told right away."

She took a deep breath in disbelief and conceded, "Yes, Sir, right away."

As she got up to leave, she asked, "Will that be all, Sir?"

"No, come here," he had a sly look on his face.

She walked over and stood in front of him. He rose from his chair and held her face in his hands.

"Please, do not take me for granted," he said. "It would tear me apart."

He took her hand and placed it on the right side of his hip, where he carried his license firearm. He looked into her eyes, as if making a statement, one he wanted to make sure got across to her. She remained still as he deeply kissed her. He once again whispered in her ear...

"You belong to me. Do you understand that?"

She pulled away, looked him in the eyes, and replied, "Yes, I do, and I always will."

"Good," he said.

Just as before, Slikk handed her another envelope before she turned to leave.

"Do not be afraid to ask," he said.

"Thank you," she replied.

"See you Friday, my dear."

He had already planted his head in the pile of papers on his desk, which clearly meant the decision was already made for her.

"Yes, sir." She replied.

She went back to her desk to find Shanique and Ms. Beckford in deep conversation, which she truly believed was about her.

"Well, Alesha, you were missing from your desk for quite some time," said Ms. Beckford.

"Yes, ma'am, and I remember mentioning to you that I would be," replied Alesha.

Shanique went back to her office, while Ms. Beckford headed to Slikk's. Alesha was told later by another staff member that Ms. Beckford could be heard having a heated conversation with him.

Alesha smiled, as she knew that once more it must be about her.

She came into work the following day to an atmosphere that was overtaken by tension. She stepped into the office and noticed Ms. Beckford coming out of Slikk's office with a package in hand. To Alesha, it looked as if that's where her mornings began.

"Good morning, Alesha," she said, smiling.

"Good morning, Ms. Beckford."

"Isn't it a beautiful morning?" she asked, with a smirk on her face.

Alesha was puzzled by her sudden change in demeanor. She wondered what could have placed her in such a vibrant mood. She knew whatever it was had something to do with her time spent in Slikk's office, but she decided that she would make the best of the day and preserve her peace.

Her day went on without much interference. Even if only for one day, she was left alone, and Ms. Beckford's voice was unheard. She saw this as her day-pass, but she felt jealousy taking over her moments of joy.

The phone rang.

"Hello," Alesha answered.

"Can you come to my office please, Alesha?" Slikk asked.

"Why... so you can tell me crap about what you did to put that smile on Ms. Beckford's face?"

"Excuse me?" Slikk replied.

"Sorry, you are right," said Alesha. "And no, I will not be able to come to your office Sir; my work needs to get done."

"Young lady, I need to see you."

"Is it about the work, sir?"

There was silence at Slikk's end.

"I did not think so Sir," said Alesha.

She saw that the girl sitting across from her was listening in on her conversation. She took into consideration that Ms. Beckford always seem to get an earful of everything, so she wondered if her conversation would make its way back to her ears. She thought for a moment before deciding that she did not give a damn anymore as to who heard what. After all, they've now all seem to turn on her for the mere belief of her being in a relationship with Slikk.

Alesha drowned herself in work, which seemed to be piling up. She was so caught up that she didn't notice Slikk passing her desk on his way to his director's meeting. Her concentration was soon broken by the ringing of her extension. She looked down to see that it was Mr. A. Black.

"Good day, Mr. Black. How may I help you?" Alesha answered.

"Alesha, can you come to my office, please?" he asked.

"I'll be there right away, sir."

As she made her way to the door, she felt uncomfortable because she had never been called to any director's office, other than Slikk's. And she knew their conversations were never about the job.

She knocked on the door and was invited in. She realized that she was part of an already seated panel. Her heart pounded with anxiety as she sat. Mentally, she struggled to figure out why she would be called to a meeting of which Slikk and Ms. Beckford were a part.

She saw that both Mr. Blacks were also in attendance.

"Do not be frightened Alesha" assured Mr. D. Black. "This is nothing for you to worry about."

She looked around the room and saw an unhappy Ms. Beckford covering her mouth with one hand, while her Assistant Kayon sat close by with a look of uncertainty. Slikk sat with his legs crossed, as if he already knew what would be said.

"Alesha, I know you are anxious as to why you have been called here," Mr. A. Black chimed in, "Well, I will not keep you in the dark much longer. By now, you all know there is an open position in accounting to be filled immediately. We have given it much consideration and decided by seniority, as well as experience who would be the best fit— Kayon."

Kayon was visibly astonished, which meant she had no prior knowledge of this. A smile spread across Ms. Beckford's face; after all, Kayon had assisted her for years.

"With that being said, Ms. Beckford will be without an assistant. Alesha, by the level of work you have done for this company, we offer you the spot for Ms. Beckford's new assistant. I know this will mean a lot to you, and you have come a far way. You will put your all in whatever is given to you to do, as you have always done."

Alesha looked at Mr. A. Black in disbelief.

"Thank you, Sir, I will."

She turned to see Slikk sporting a smile. As for Ms. Beckford, she could do nothing to hide the anger she was feeling.

"Do I have a say in this sir?" asked Ms. Beckford, trying to suppress her rage.

"The decision is already made. I do not see anyone else fitting for this position Ms. Beckford. Do you?" asked Mr. A. Black.

"Yes, I do," replied Ms. Beckford.

"With all due respect, Ms. Beckford, this is out of your hands, Mr. Black and I have already made the decision," Mr. D. Black's response was firm.

As Ms. Beckford rose from her seat and charged towards the door, she casted a disgusted glance at Slikk. She showed everyone that she didn't know the true meaning of work ethics.

"Excuse me, ma'am, this meeting is not finished," Mr. A. Black attempted to halt her in her tracks.

"With all due respect, Sir, I was not given a say in this decision and therefore, I have to leave." She walked out and slammed the door behind her.

They all sat in silence, as if trying to make sense of the disrespect just displayed.

The directors all looked at each other. "I will deal with this tomorrow," said Mr. A. Black. "I want to congratulate you both on your promotions. I expect that you will both make us proud. You're dismissed."

"Thank you, Sir," they both replied and walked out.

Alesha went to get her bag because it was now time to leave. She saw no trace of Ms. Beckford, but fully grasped the depth of her anger and disagreement towards her for being chosen for the position. She waited to see Slikk come out but soon realized the meeting continued even though they had been dismissed.

With joy in her heart, but doubts in her mind, Alesha packed her belongings and headed home. She decided to keep her seemingly great news hidden from her family for now because something was amiss about all that had taken place. She got undressed and rested for a bit. Until her phone rang.

"Hello."

"Hi, my Dear"

"Hello, Slikk."

"You must be so excited?"

"Not really."

"Why? You have been promoted!"

"Depends on how you look at the word 'promoted.' I know you had something to do with it, and I thank you for that."

"Thank me for what? I did nothing. You earned your promotion on your own, and you deserve it. I am very proud of you."

"Thank you... sir... but Ms. Beckford certainly does not think so."

"Who cares what she thinks? The decision was not hers to make, and the directors made the right one. It is time for you to think of your own interest because trust me, no one in this company is looking out for you... well, except me, of course. Ms. Beckford has made her way, now it is time for you to make yours. Understand?"

"Yes." I think so," replied Alesha.

"Good. Tomorrow, come prepared for a new beginning and do not make me look bad. I am counting on you. I am also counting on being with you again. I can't stop thinking about what happened between us the last time and how you made me feel."

"I wish I had an idea of how I made you feel. I can see it has had some kind of impact on you. Glad you feel that way Slikk," replied Alesha.

"And always will, dear. So, when can I see you again?" asked Slikk.

"You have still not explained Ms. Beckford's early visit to your office, one that gave her some kind of boost."

"Again, Alesha! What should I explain? See me Friday and I will tell you everything."

Although she had every reason to be mad at Slikk, she somehow struggled with saying so. So instead she said, "Ok, I will."

Alesha faced the rest of her days in uncertainty. Ms. Beckford struggled with introducing her to staff as her new assistant, because she had no say in the decision, while Alesha struggled with the fact that she now had to work with Ms. Beckford, who would be the one to have the final say on everything she did. She kept Slikk's words close to heart and made the best of an uneasy situation.

Ms. Beckford was still at war with the directors, as she did not exchange words with them unless related to the job. It was only left to one's imagination, the status she truly held in the company owned by two individuals, both males.

"Alesha, I am running out of the office for a while. I expect you to hold the fort until I get back," said Ms. Beckford.

"Hold the fort..." Alesha thought. "How will I do that with no training as to what exactly I am supposed to do?" Alesha wondered if this was a direct attempt by Ms. Beckford to see her fail.

"Yes ma'am, I will do just that," she decided not to verbalize her actual thoughts.

"And please do so from your desk, which means you must be present there," said Ms. Beckford.

"Yes, ma'am, as always," Alesha replied.

Ms. Beckford threw her bag across her shoulder and gave Alesha a disapproving glance before stepping through the door.

Alesha smiled, even though she had not been briefed on the duties expected of her. She knew what needed to be done to have a fully functional office, as she had been doing so all along without any recognition whatsoever. She did exactly what was asked by taking charge of the day's activities while adding her flair of professionalism as best as she could.

Ms. Beckford would be searching for a reason to put her in the line of fire, and Slikk would be blamed for any mistakes she made. He was thought to be the one that got her in the position so, she made sure to do what was necessary for a well-organized department and in the same breath, hear "well done" for her accomplishments.

Time flew by quickly. Alesha found her days a bit more hectic, as she had to make sure her desk was always cleared before leaving for school. She hid that fact from Ms. Beckford, because she knew the problem it would pose if she got wind that she was trying to uplift herself academically. This awareness would add fury to her fire and would prove unbearable for Alesha.

For her, things were looking much brighter now that she was enrolled in school. She sought to secure a career in the field of Accounting since that was what she chose to study in school. She also made time on weekends to take driving lessons, all at Slikk's request, who made it very clear that moving forward was his hope for her.

She marveled at the fact that he paid interest in her well-being. And even though she worried about her relationship with him affecting her job, she still gave it all she had to offer and tried her best to keep all involvement with him private. However, she could not bypass the many rumors floating around the office about him. She wondered if the rumors were the truth just waiting to be revealed. To matters worse, Alesha began to see a change in Slikk's behavior. He became somewhat withdrawn, an obvious difference from his palpable enthusiasm whenever he saw her. It was as if he had changed overnight. Ms. Beckford's frequent visits to his office became more noticeable and she witnessed the frequent lunch dates shared between them both. She even noticed that at times, Shanique became part of the newfound joy. Gone were the days when Slikk would deliberately walk pass her desk just for a glimpse of her. Instead, it was Ms. Beckford's extension that was being bombarded with his calls and witnessing how happy this made her became painful for Alesha.

Alesha recalled overhearing Ms. Beckford and Shanique planning an all-inclusive weekend for Slikk's birthday, and in that instant, she knew whatever plan they both had was being executed with success. Alesha knew she was losing the battle to have Slikk as a part of her life forever, but she also knew she had to try, even if it was for the last time.

She picked up the phone and dialed his extension number.

"Sir, may I have a word with you?" Alesha said

"I am a bit busy, but you may come," Slikk replied.

This response came as a shock to her because she could not believe he had become unavailable to her. As she walked towards his door, she glanced at Shanique's office and saw that she was sporting a huge smile.

"Come please, Alesha," he said as she knocked on the door.

"How might I help you today?" asked Slikk.

He had his head down as if the pile of papers he studied were of more importance than anything she was about to say.

"Sir, can you at least acknowledge my presence?"

"I can ride and whistle you know. That's a part of what makes me good at my job. Go ahead, Alesha, I am listening."

She was now sure she was no longer at the center of anything for him.

"I do not understand what is happening." Her tone was confrontational.

"What are you talking about?" He seemed perplexed.

"Slikk, I am talking about you and Ms. Beckford –and also Shanique."

"Young lady remember we are at work. It is more appropriate for both of us if you address me professionally," said Slikk.

"Well, Mr. Durrant, you never had a problem before with me calling you Slikk," she replied.

"Well, there's a time and place for everything, and here and now calls for professionalism," said Slikk.

"Sir, are you seeing Ms. Beckford? Are you seeing Shanique? It is very clear there is some kind of rekindled bond between you three."

"Alesha, I will not discuss this with you again. How many times must we go through this? I am annoyed that I have to explain myself over and over again."

She stared at him. It was as if his attitude towards her had become vile. She was about to tell him her real thoughts when she was interrupted by a loud knock on the door.

"Come," said Slikk.

Shanique pushed the door open and stepped in. She seemed upset to see Alesha standing in front of Slikk. She stood by the side of his desk, with both hands folded, and her back turned to Alesha, a gesture Alesha immediately took as a sign of disrespect to her.

"Yes, Shanique, what is it?" Slikk asked.

"Sir, I need to go over the bank reconciliation with you. I need the information to be sent off to the bank."

"Can you give me a few minutes, please? I will call you in a bit," replied Slikk.

"No Sir, now! Ms. Beckford is also awaiting the information to give to Mr. Black."

"I see," he replied, with his focus now fixed on Alesha.

She now understood the meaning of being embarrassed because she took that as her cue to leave. With her head hung low, and her eyes filled with tears, she walked out.

"Thank you, sir," Shanique said as she left.

***

Alesha's days passed with everyone else seemingly happy. She heard talks of Slikk rekindling his romance with the woman he once made an outcast, Ms. Beckford. There were rumors of him being under some kind of "spell." She believed whatever it was had a strong effect on him; strong enough to make him lose interest in her.

Even the Directors joined in the talks about the reunion. Alesha's heart melted in pain. She worried about her enrollment in school and wondered if Slikk would make good on his promise of financial support, which she needed to succeed in her endeavors. Nothing seemed to take precedence over the tension that took over the office. Alesha felt abandoned. She was now Ms. Beckford's target even more than before.

Calls and messages from Slikk had become no more. She fought with feelings of rejection, as she watched Slikk and Ms. Beckford getting much closer. Depression became a part of Alesha's days. She pretended to focus only on the requirements of her job, but it was difficult to keep that show going. She was constantly reminded of how quickly Ms. Beckford had taken her spot.

She was now convinced that the only way she would get any peace of mind was to be away from everyone who played their part in the nightmare she was trapped in. Her only solace was that she had accumulated vacation time. Time away from work would be a great way to think about what she had gone through and how to cope with it all. So she went to speak to Ms. Beckford.

"Ms. Beckford, I would like to put in for my vacation leave," said Alesha.

"How many days are you planning to take?" asked Ms. Beckford.

"Well, ma'am, seeing that I have my leave coming up, along with the last two times I didn't take any, at least three weeks."

"Well, let me check your file to make certain that you are entitled to the time you claim to have."

Ms. Beckford headed toward Shanique's office where employee files were kept, and Alesha went back to her desk. Ms. Beckford was away for a while, but Alesha convinced herself it was only to verify the information. Quite some time elapsed before Ms. Beckford returned to Alesha's desk. "Well, Alesha, I was prepared to grant your request, until Shanique pointed out that the only time you are entitled to, is time you have coming up. Previous times to which you refer were already used."

"Excuse me, ma'am, that information is incorrect. Can you please recall me having the conversation with you about not taking time off? And you were the one who told me that I did not have to rush in doing so, as they would be given to me whenever I was ready," insisted Alesha.

"Alesha please remember that Shanique is the one currently in charge of all the files and would be able to tell whether or not one is entitled to time requested. Please, take into consideration that documents do not lie."

"So, what are you saying Ms. Beckford? That I am lying, hence I cannot get the time I am entitled to?"

"Of course, you can, but as I've said, only for that of your upcoming leave," replied Ms. Beckford.

"I do not know what is going to happen, but I am taking the time I am owed, and what I am entitled to." Alesha was defiant.

"Are you telling me how to run this place, is that it?" Ms. Beckford's tone was now high pitched.

"Ms. Beckford, I have no control over how you interpret the words that come from my mouth. But the only way I see out of this is to take my own justice, since none will be given to me."

"You are downright rude! I will see what Mr. A. Black has to say about your behavior," she exclaimed vehemently.

She walked away from Alesha and went into her office to make a call to him; he was out of the office for the day.

Alesha sat patiently knowing no justice would come her way. How could it, since she had offended the office's 'first lady'? As she waited with everyone else looking on, Ms. Beckford returned with a pleased look on her face.

"Well, you said you wanted your time, so you can take all the time you require. Mr. Black has decided to allow you to go home until he can further investigate what has just taken place. When a decision is reached, you will be contacted."

Chattering was heard among the rest of the staff. Alesha could almost feel their piercing stares in her back as she gathered her belongings and headed towards the door. She was once again stopped by Ms. Beckford's voice.

"Please remember to leave the company's phone."

She handed the phone to a staff member seated near the exit, as she had no desire to go anywhere near the 'witch'.

***

The night fell quickly. She sat at home thinking about what had taken place, and how badly she felt about letting Slikk down. She searched for an answer to how differently she could have handled the situation, but it was too late for that. She buried her feelings, as she could not allow anyone to find out the true reason why she was home. She had done nothing wrong but also knew her involvement with Slikk had put her in Ms. Beckford's line of fire. Anyone who had been there would know that there is no escaping that judgment.

As her worried days passed, she tried to come to a conclusion as to why Slikk had not made any effort to contact her. He must be aware of her mishap with Ms. Beckford. She struggled through the weeks now upon her with no sympathy from anyone. Even though she already knew what Mr. Black's decision would be, she waited anxiously for the call. Nothing but a spark of hope was left in her grasp. There was one person who showed, in some way, that he cared about her well-being –Slikk's good friend, Caine.

Alesha called up Caine to tell him what had unfolded. He expressed shock and anger that Slikk did not care enough to find out how she had been treated. He then told her that Slikk had severed all ties with him as well

247

because he was upset with him for wrecking his diesel truck, the one he affectionately called Betsy. Caine comforted her the best way he could. He told her that whatever she and Slikk were going through was just a phase. He encouraged her to stay positive while it lasted. She told him she was not sure about being called back for her job, but he laughed and assured her that would all be taken care of. He told her of the many times he'd heard Slikk express his love for her, and how he would make sure she never wanted for anything. She was puzzled that Slikk expressed his feelings for her to a friend, but now that she was in real need, he hadn't picked up the phone to comfort her. Nevertheless, she thought she owed it to him to let him know what had happened.

She finally built up the courage to give him a call.

"Yes, hello," Slikk answered.

"Hi Slikk," replied Alesha.

His tone deepened, as if annoyed.

"Yes, Alesha?" Slikk replied.

"I know you must have heard all by now, and you are probably disappointed, but you could have called."

"Excuse me? I have been very busy during the days because we are now in the auditing period. I have no time for myself, and no time to waste on your silly calls."

"Silly calls? Don't you see? Ms. Beckford finally accomplished her goal of getting me fired," said Alesha.

"And what do you think I can do about that? I warned you. I told you to keep your mouth shut no matter what she said. You chose not to listen, so you must deal with the consequences on your own. I cannot help you, and I told the directors not to get involved. Do you think I would risk losing my job over this? Janice has no say in whatever happens to you, and the same goes for Shanique. You did this to yourself. You will not be re-called for the job. Janice will contact you with a date to pick up your last paycheque. It's just a pity Alesha, the Directors had plans to give you a raise, and uniforms. You've made a mess of everything.

"Uniform?" Alesha blurted. 'Is that the best you can come up with?"

She wasted no time letting her tears flow.

"Do you see what I mean? You are so weak. Why are you crying?" asked Slikk.

"Slikk, you are not the same person I met a few months ago; it's as if this side of you was hidden and waiting to show itself. I need your help. I am down financially, and the second half of my school fee is now due. My exams are coming up and the college will not allow me to sit them if I have outstanding fees. Can I at least get the money you promised me to clear my finances?"

"What money? I have no money to give anyone. I work hard for what I have, and so should anyone else who wants what I have. You'll have to find that help elsewhere, anywhere, just not from me," Slikk's tone was not comforting.

"Slikk, please! Mr. Durrant. You are the one who told me to enroll; otherwise, I wouldn't have. I knew I would not have the money for that. What about driving lessons and the car you promised you would have bought me?" sobbed Alesha.

There was a burst of laughter on the other end of the phone line.

"Well, at least you still have a sense of humor. I told you I cannot afford to put you through college, yet you question me about buying a car. That there is the reason I always had Janice around. She has proven herself to be the cleverest of the lot. Anyway, I have to go to a meeting. I wish you the best in life and hope it all works out. And please, do not try getting in touch with me. Goodbye."

Alesha held the phone to her ear, even when Slikk had hung up. She was sure she was in a dream, one she needed so badly to wake up from.

She struggled with Slikk's final words in the months that followed. Before now, he had always kept his word. She hoped that he would somehow come to his senses about what she meant to him. She soon realized that hope of getting anything promised by him would never materialize.

***

Time did nothing to mend her shattered heart. She heard nothing from Slikk. Even when she went to pick up that last paycheque, it was as if she never existed at that company. The only thing Alesha took solace in was a photograph of him she kept hidden, one she used as a reminder of what a monster truly looked like.

As the months passed, she struggled with the mere fact of her existence and with the expense of trying to continue her studies. There was nothing she could do to ease her woes. She was often called to the Accounting Department of the college for not being able to make payment. She had to plea for mercy on several occasions when she could not come up with the funds to pay for her exams. She recalled one occasion when she broke down in tears in front of the Accountant.

"I know it's hard not being able to sit your examinations, after all the effort you have placed in getting to this point. But you have to understand we have a school to run, and if we give a pass to every student who is finding it hard to pay, then the school will be out of business. Do you understand what I'm saying?" asked the Accountant.

"I do," Alesha muttered.

"Listen to me girl! You have life, so you can overcome this obstacle. Do not give up, let this moment be a part of your story," replied the Accountant.

Alesha knew she had to find a way out of all this, even though she was told to enroll in school by Slikk, she knew she was the one who would have to see it through. She had no one to turn to, and she knew family members would not be able to assist as they had troubles of their own. Now memories of how being employed had made her life much easier, came rushing back, and even though she knew there was no going back to that company, not being there didn't make it any easier.

Alesha found herself replaying all that Slikk had said to her about not making it in life. She wanted so much to prove him wrong, even if it meant pouring out her heart to him once more. After all, he was the only one she knew that was in the position to give her a financial breakthrough. And the fact that he cared for her once, gave her hope that those feelings still existed, and she was willing to take one more chance finding out if her beliefs could truly become reality.

Now was her moment of truth. She knew she couldn't contact Slikk on his cell phone as he had warned her to desist or else her number would be blocked, and she knew him well enough to know that he always made good on his words. She had to find another means of getting to him without anyone knowing her true identity. Alesha picked up the phone and dialed the company's number.

"Good afternoon, how may I assist?" The receptionist answered.

"Hi, Good day to you. May I please be transferred to Mr. Durrant's office?" Alesha asked.

"May I ask whose calling?" replied the receptionist.

"My name is Mrs. Myers. I am very much interested in doing some business with your company, and I was told to contact Mr. Durrant, to get some information."

Even though the receptionist knew that Mr. Durrant would not be the first point of contact for any individual interested in purchasing products from the company, she also knew he played an important role in assisting any potential customer with information as it relates to them becoming a part of the customer base, as well as providing them with information that would not be accessible to other employees.

The receptionist told her to hold the line while she checked if Mr. Durrant was available to take her call. Alesha's heart raced heavily as she wondered if Slikk would come to the phone, and if he did, would he hang up when he realized she was the one pretending to be Mrs. Myers.

Alesha heard a beep on the line and knew she was being transferred.

"Hello, good day, how might I be of assistance?" said the voice on the other end.

"Hi Mr. Durrant, it's me," replied Alesha.

"Alesha? Why would you pretend to be someone else, and why are you calling me? Thought I made it clear to you that you have to stop contacting me."

"Please Slikk, just listen. I really need your help. I promise I will never bother you again."

"Ok. You have five minutes. As you know I am a very busy man, I do not have time for your silly behaviors. That is one of the reasons I severed all ties with you; your immaturity was driving me crazy."

Alesha wanted so badly to tell him what she really thought of him, but she knew he would not give her the chance to get that far. So, she kept her cool and acted her part well, a humble soul in need of dire help.

"Well Alesha, I'm waiting. Your five minutes is almost up, what is it that you want?"

"Slikk, help me please, I need to pay off my debts at school. Exams are coming up and I will not be allowed to sit any. I know you are not obligated to assist me in any way whatsoever, but please remember the only reason I enrolled was because you promised to finance me through to the end. I am not asking to be a part of your life again. I'm just asking for your help to get back on my feet, I am willing to repay you whenever that happens if that is what you want."

Alesha's words were suddenly interrupted by a burst of laughter.

"The only thing I would be able to assist you with right now is recommending you to a good psychiatrist because you are clearly delusional," he mocked. "How many times must I tell you that I do not care about your woes? What must I do to make it clear to you that I will not be financing your school funds anymore? I gave you the start, now you need to finish it, and I do not care how you do it, as long as you do it without me. And Alesha, if you contact me again you will be deeply sorry. Go find yourself a job. Besides, it will take a while for you to get me out of your system, trust me. I wish you all the best."

Alesha realized there was nothing she could say that would change the way he felt about her, so she decided to get a few words in before never hearing from him again.

"You dirty man!" Alesha shouted, "You really believe you will get away with what you have done to me. Slikk, you mark my words I will live to hear of your demise, you will be rewarded for all you have dished out to me. You are going to reap what you sow; I promise you."

"Alesha, mi a bad man, just ask Caine. He will tell you, you can't threaten me. Be careful, you don't have a clue who you're playing with. You best stay in your hole if you know what's good for you," replied Slikk.

"Hello, hello, Slikk please," Alesha screamed as she realized he was no longer at the other end of the line.

Now, she had to face the bitter reality that he was never going to let her back in his life, nor would he assist her with any of her financial woes. She realized she would have to find a way to get herself back on track, but how would she do that? She had no one to turn to and she could not even trust herself.

***

Time went by and Alesha remained unemployed and still puzzled about how to move forward. She was still brainstorming how she would pay for her exams, as they were only a week away, and by now she should have collected her timecard, which is the pass for her to enter the examination room. She took solace in the fact that she had applied for a few jobs and was hoping even one employer would give her a call. She often wondered what her explanation would be when faced with the question of her reason for leaving her last job, but she decided when that time came, she would deal with it.

Suddenly, Alesha's thoughts were interrupted by her cell phone ringing.

"Hello," Alesha answered.

"Hi Alesha, how have you been?"

"Caine," Alesha responded.

"Yes, I have been thinking about you, wondering how you have been coping since the last time we spoke. I still struggle to understand why Slikk did what he did to you. You didn't deserve any of it. And to make matters worse he was the one who pushed for you to be with him. I do not respect his actions at all."

Alesha fumbled to comment on what Caine had said. Her voice cracked as she could not hold back the tears.

"Don't cry Alesha," Caine consoled her over the phone "Whatever it is, I will help you."

"I know you have good intentions, but this one I have to work out on my own," replied Alesha.

"Alesha you have been through enough with Slikk. It's time you allowed someone to be there for you, someone who wants nothing in return. I am here now. Let me be that person. What's wrong? Tell me."

"Ok." she replied, "I have exams coming up next week and I cannot sit them because I have outstanding funds; I have nowhere to turn Caine. I tried once more getting help from Slikk, but again he insulted me. I still haven't found a job, I have no money, I just don't know what to do, I feel so ashamed."

"How long do you have left in school?' asked Caine.

"One year. So that's two (2) semesters. And I really dream of graduating."

"You will," said Caine. I will give you the money to pay for your upcoming exams, as well as the money for the rest of the time you have left in school. Just tell me how much it is.

"What!" Alesha exclaimed. "Caine, would you really do that for me? That's too much…Can you afford that?"

"Alesha, I have been rolling with Slikk for many years. Do you really think I wouldn't make sure I am provided for? Don't worry about me finding the money. And as I've told you before, you didn't deserve any of what Slikk did to you. I have been his friend for so long, and he turned his back on me, but I thought he would be less harsh with you, because of how he told me he felt about you. I believe we are both victims of Slikk's drive for power, but I can tell you this, he will not get away with what he has done this time, I promise you."

"What do you mean?" asked Alesha.

"You will see," replied Caine. "Now, how much should I give you for everything? I need an account number so I can wire the money to you. Oh, and Alesha, before I forget, you have an interview two days from now.

"No, I don't. I have applied to a few places but have not received a call as yet."

"Well, you have not applied here. Do you think Slikk is the only one that has friends in high places? I am the one that introduced him to most of his acquaintances. Slikk could have gotten you a job if he wanted to. Well, I want to, so you just prepare yourself. My friend needs an Office Manager for his business. I told him I have just the right fit, and I know with your experience you will do great at the job."

Caine could hear sobbing at the other end of the line.

"How can I ever repay you for all your help Caine?"

"Just graduate, be successful at your job and whenever you can, help someone else. And I will be at your graduation. Now, remember to send me the account number and the amount to deposit as soon as you hang up. You will be hearing from me soon."

"Thank you so much, Caine, I will not disappoint you, I promise," replied Alesha. And with that, she hung up the phone and fell to her knees and instantly began praying. She had hoped help would come, but she never imagined it would be through Caine.

***

It was finally here, Alesha's graduation day. A year had flown by so quickly. Her life was now bright and happy. She smiled as she remembered that Caine would be present, as well as her friends she had made at her new place of work. They promised they would be in the front row, to make sure they did not miss her collecting her certificate. As promised, there they were taking pictures of her as she walked across the stage. Graduating with honors even added more excitement to her already happy mood.

Alesha didn't need to look far, as Caine's presence was evident. After all, he was the one with the loudest applause. As she looked over at him, she saw a familiar face sitting right next to him. In disbelief, she collected her certificate and walked off the stage. She wanted desperately for the ceremony to be over so she could be sure her eyes were not deceiving her, but she held her composure and waited patiently. When it was all over, Alesha was surrounded by her friends who couldn't wait to congratulate her, and she made sure they all got their turn at doing just that. She then walked over to where Caine was waiting with his associate.

"Mr. D. Black!" Alesha exclaimed, "What are you doing here and how did you know I would be graduating at all, moreover today?"

"Isn't it obvious? Caine reached out to me and told me. Alesha, I know this is of no consolation to you, but I am truly sorry for the way you were treated. Believe me, I tried talking my brother out of letting you go, but he was adamant, as Ms. Beckford told him it's either you go, or she would. Believe me, when you left, we had so many issues at the office. It became clear in that instant, that you were one whose contribution really made a difference."

"It's ok Sir. I understand. And believe me, I am past all that now. I now see why things happened the way they did. It has all led me to here, this moment. And Caine, I truly thank you for that." Alesha expressed joyfully.

"Don't thank me. You were the one who finished school; I had nothing to do with that," replied Caine.

"Alesha, I have something to ask you," said Mr. Black

"Of course, go right ahead," replied Alesha.

In your time at the company, did you get any hint about Slikk was stealing?"

"Stealing? Stealing what? What are you talking about?"

"I thought you would have heard."

"Heard what?" replied Alesha.

Both Caine and Mr. Black turned to look at each other.

"Slikk was in jail. We found out that he was embezzling millions from the company. He was handcuffed on the compound. He was a spectacle for all to see. And his secretary went right along with him. She made a scene about him being arrested, and we found proof that she was also involved in his wrongdoings,"

"What! When did this happen?" asked Alesha.

"It was two weeks ago, replied Mr. Black."

Alesha immediately looked over at Caine, as his words came rushing back to her. "Slikk is going to pay for what he has done to you." Oh my God! Now she knew where those envelopes with cash came from.

"Slikk, stealing? I just can't believe!" she replied in shock.

"Yes, and I wanted him to go to prison, but Ms. Beckford bawled her eyes out to my brother and assured him all the money would be repaid. It seems he had been stealing from the company for years. Only God knows how much he has taken from us." Mr. Black's expression was grim.

"I am shocked," said Alesha, "I had no idea Slikk was stealing. I truly thought he was too proud to be caught doing something like that."

"Well, he had everyone fooled," replied Mr. Black. "So Alesha, I just came to see you graduate, and to let you know I am so happy for you. You are truly a fighter. I have to run now, but please keep in touch."

"I will Sir. Thank you for coming," replied Alesha.

Mr. Black shook Caine's hand and walked off.

Alesha could not wait to get a word in with Caine. "What! I really can't believe this. Now, I know how he managed to be so successful. I wonder if that's where all those envelopes with money were coming from."

"Alesha, whatever Slikk did, you had no idea. He was just too greedy, and it had to come to an end one day. Well, that day is now."

"Caine, I have to ask, did you have anything to do with this, and have you heard from him?"

"It doesn't matter how they found out; it just matters that they did. And you of all persons should know that he deserves whatever he gets. And yes, I have heard from him since all this unfolded. I believe he truly forgot he cut me off because he called wanting to meet up. Slikk only uses people whenever he sees fit. Frankly, I am glad all this unfolded with me and him, I have now learnt who he really is."

"Now stop wasting your thoughts on Slikk. Look at you Alesha! I am so proud of you, and I have also heard that you are doing very well at your job. I knew you would be able to pull it off. Slikk has no idea what he has lost."

"Thank you, Caine. But I could not do any of it without you. I do want to repay you for your kindness. How can I?" asked Alesha.

"I have already told you. Just pay it forward. You owe me nothing. I would do it for you all over again," replied Caine. They hugged, and he whispered the words, "I will always be here for you."

With time, Alesha finally forgot all about Slikk and his reign of terror on her. She had never been happier. And she made a vow to keep it that way. She was at home one evening preparing dinner when her cell phone rang.

"Hello," Alesha answered.

"Hi Alesha, how have you been?"

She could not believe the voice she was hearing at the other end of the line.

"Slikk?"

"Yes, it's me. Alesha, before you say anything, I called to say I am very sorry for all that was done to you. Through all of it, you truly acted as the wonderful individual you are. I made a huge mistake letting you go. Alesha, please forgive me. I want to see you." Slikk sounded desperate.

"I can't believe I'm hearing this. I would have done anything to hear those words before now. Now, hearing them makes me sick. First of all, if you are wondering if I heard what happened to you, I sure did. And no, I don't feel sorry for you one bit," Alesha used this opportunity to replay his very words. "I wish you all the best in life, and I hope it all works out for you. Do not try contacting me again as you will be blocked. Oh, and Slikk, before I forget, I have one last thing to say to you. Isn't Karma a B…..?"

Alesha laughed out loudly, then hung up the phone. She knew he would realize that his own words had come back to haunt him.

"Isn't life dandy?"

Men, we are always there, even when you showed that you are incapable of seeing and appreciating ur presence. We still stood with you, because we know you are the completion of the story, you are the reason for our strength. You are the reason we have taken up the fallen baton, to finish the race. Our journey was made possible because of all the different paths you have forced us to take, yet the ending is the same. Your games, your hurt, our sacrifices have become and will forever be our told stories.

Questions:

1. Where did Alesha go wrong?

2. Was it OK for Slikk not to tell her that he had no intention of keeping his promises?

3. Was he right to choose his career over hers and her quest to complete college?

4. Should she have seen this coming and gotten out of the relationship earlier?

5. In the end, did Slikk deserve what he got, or was he betrayed by a friend?

A Player's Game

I t takes little or nothing for a man to inflict hurt upon a woman. He does so whenever he chooses.

Perhaps he didn't know that his children would turn their backs on him for tearing apart the happy world he spent so much time creating for them. Still he allowed it to happen because in his eyes a minute of boastful pleasure meant more than a lifetime of untold happiness.

We are left to wonder what his thoughts are when he looks at himself in the mirror. Is it that from his perspective he sees:

1. A manipulator of the games- Ones he plays in his relationship
2. A breaker of rules- The very ones he expects her to follow and live by?
3. A taker of hearts- With no regard for the victims left broken, and the shattered pieces to be picked up along the way?

Finally, is it that he sees himself as the true winner because when all has been accomplished, he will now become the conqueror in the war of love. Could it be that, if such a man should observe his very behavior through a woman's eyes, he would be astonished to see that:

- The games he so desperately believes he has manipulated will eventually be the end to his happy life?

- The rules he thought he so successfully broke were designed and expected to be broken, hence he is just a newcomer to a game that has been played far before his time?

- The lies that took time and effort to construct, were already realized and anticipated? Only to decide whether or not they will be accepted.

- The hearts he continues to take as trophies of his victory have already withstood the terror of hurt and pain, hence it has little or no reaction to the hurt he inflicts? So, is it that you have truly completed your mission, or is it that you are allowed to continue taking women's souls only because it's you whom we truly love?

A player's dream must become his reality, so he will do what is necessary to get his way, which becomes his truth, not foreseeing what awaits him ahead, which is his demise. In his moment of conquest, what he sees instead is another heart to be crushed, another tear to be cried, another score to be settled and of course, another woman to be scorned.

But how does a woman move past the terror that has rained down upon her?

Her life will be devastated by her man's actions. Her world will become distorted by the ongoing pain he has inflicted upon her. She will find herself asking: "What have I done to deserve such torment?"

Yet in all her anguish, she still somehow manages to:

1. Smile at her kids every morning.

2. Make sure her husband's clients are greeted with a smile before entering their place of business.

3. Manage the account which will ensure all expectations are met to enable the easy flow of the day's activities.

4. Assist him with all the information necessary for a successful presentation to his potential clients.

5. Finally, at the end of her well managed day, she makes certain she is present for the dinner, one she spent the time and effort to prepare, but only after making sure the children have done all that is required of them, and they are set to take on another day at school.

A player believes that what he does is only because that is how he was created. Yet, he expects his woman to disregard her thoughts of creation to accommodate his world of necessities, ones which allow him to gain and maintain total control of her, in his well-created world. He will make sure he professes his complete love for her only, giving all assurance that he is the one she can completely trust. He will show her that he is the bearer of truth, the reliever of hurt and the only giver of her happiness.

But if a woman looks closely, she can see the real meaning behind a man's smiles whenever he looks at her. She can hear the obvious doubt in his words, feel the pain in his touch, and painfully smell another woman's perfume on his shirt. Everything he does is only for his happiness.

When a man looks at a woman, the first thing he sees that makes an impression on him is her physical appearance; and of course, that is in fact, human nature. But could it be that within that look, he has already decided if she will become his new project, or be extended mercy this time around?

Does a woman see it the same way when her eyes meet her newfound crush? With just one glance, she will instantly know if there is any form of attraction to a man. But he may never know how she feels, because of how brilliantly she covers up that truth. She knows that if she allows him to realize that just looking at him makes her unable to speak or even find the strength to breathe, she would have given him a free pass for a lifetime of chains, disappointments and continuous pain, a pain she never knew would be caused by the man she gave the chance to share her life. She knows that when he does anything for her, there is always an ulterior motive behind it.

The motives behind a man's actions:

When he lies - He does so to make sure that all possibilities of the truth are erased at any cost, even at that of his own life. He breaks the truth into many pieces so that whenever necessary, he can fit a piece into any small crack found in the story he is about to tell. He finds a way to tell some parts of the truth wrapped intimately in his lies, ensuring it all comes together perfectly to justify any insecurity a woman may have. But within this planning and effort, he will not realize that he has openly communicated the truth, the very same thing he fought so hard to keep hidden.

When he explains - He does so boastfully, because he wants her to believe that he has a level of respect for her and that his actions were for a well-meant reason. He will want her to believe, he meant to hurt or put her down. He hopes that she will feel relieved and assured even when the explanation he has gust given is yet another of his lies. She will now be left with no other option than to accept all his wrongs.

When he hurts – A player's hurt is unbearable for him. He has used his time and strength to construct two worlds for only his existence and pleasure, so now this unforeseen collision is a true reality. No more living on the edge, no more having his cake and eating it too, for his excitement and ego are now in jeopardy. How does he rebound from this? How will his happiness continue? He is lost because he only knows how to exist in both worlds. And now that one is threatened, how will he compromise? Oh, what pain has been inflicted on the just?

When he regrets – The regrets of a player will ultimately become the reason his sworn love turns into hate. When his second world is pulled out from under him, it takes him from his comfort zone. He believes that the one who ultimately brings him to this point is the one who has inflicted a wound and a reign of terror upon him. Hence, he cannot face her without being reminded of the loss she has caused him and the experiences of which she has robbed him. He will do everything in his power to recreate the world he was too quickly torn from, and this time he must succeed at any cost.

When he cries – A man cries when he finally realizes that he'll never again be looked at as the once-respected person he tried so hard to be. His games are all figured out hence, he becomes clueless as to the next move to make. He cries because his dream world of seeking after passion will now be replaced by a lifetime of reality in which his boundaries have been threatened. He is left to weep uncontrollably, because his reign of dominance will be over, forcing him to awaken to the lingering scent of the coffee.

He must face the reality of the pain he will experience when the web of deceit he has weaved is broken and unraveled, which by the way is nothing compared to the pain his counterpart underwent in watching him put it all together.

But what are the real reasons behind his tears? -Is it that a man cries when the plan with his sweetheart is compromised, and she can no longer be the reliever in his agonizing love quest? He has left her to pick up the many pieces into which her world has been shattered. She must now find solace in the fact that she is not the only causality of his harm. She now ponders what she could have done differently in becoming a more important part of his life. She fights hard to understand why he bothered to take the time to create a comfort zone when the comforter will never be there. She now believes all men portray a bond of brotherhood and justice when they seek to repay the wrong that has been done to them by the one, they see as their enemy, a woman. The same woman that does everything to fit him into her world.

What he would have her to believe – His shyness is because he truly loves her. But does he really, or is it that his real aim is to get her to think he's so taken up with her that he has no clue as to how to behave when he's in her company? Just when she's comfortable around him and finally embraces the thought that this could truly be love, he uses this feeling of safety and comfort to dig into her soul, eventually holding her hostage to her feelings. He can now finally be at ease because she belongs to him. Then finally when she becomes and addition to those before her. He can smoothly move on to his next prey.

He can always be trusted - It's a hard task for individuals in any relationship to develop and maintain trust for each other. When that goal is accomplished, it will feel as if your life is approaching completeness. But what does this sense of completion mean for a woman involved with a player? It means she puts herself, her happiness, her comfort, her all, in his hands. She believes that he will be there for her. He will play his part which will be for her amelioration. Her trust in him means she sees no other one but him; she believes he will never let her down.

This place is the hardest for any woman to reach, so it should be understood how heartbreaking it is when she looks beyond her man's faults and tries to find the best in him. She believes that all obstacles have been overcome, only to find that he had no intention of committing to her only. His only intent was for her to be solely dependent on him, so he can have her believe whatever he wanted, whenever he wanted.

He will give her preferential treatment - A woman will always receive preferential treatment when she is being pursued by any man. He will tell her that he wants her to bear his children. He will convince her that if she just allows him to experience her essence, he will be able to do the impossible. There will be no reason for her to believe that she is only a part of a plot in his book or just his next potential client because he is already successful in having her believe that he has no reason to rewrite the story that has now given him a happy ending in his tales to be told.

She's his change - He will tell her she has walked in and allowed him to forget his life before her. He can now see his new beginning. He has reached a place where he never thought existed: the happiness he only read about. She will come to feel her arms are
his only refuge, and if only they are opened to him, then he will be saved. She will believe that she is the reason he never goes back, and the reason he will never have regrets. But if this is true, why is it that it becomes so easy for him to say he has fallen out of love with her?

******

Some men condition their minds to feed their craving for happiness at all times with little or no thought for others. And if at any time they should consider taking a step back, this decision will not come as a result of their happiness being threatened.

For men, like the players in the story, their behavior now becomes predictable. It seems as though they all audition for the same role in their made-up script. Hence, the same lines are recited and brought about in the exact manner. At the end of the day, the results are still the same; we've heard it all before.

In this web of deceit called relationships, we will sometimes be left to decide who will survive and who will be at fault. Will poetic justice prevail or will lives be cut short, and dreams be shattered with the ultimate aim of being crowned as the one true player.

It is said that it is much harder for a man to find his place in society, as he is expected to play the role that is necessary to exist, while silently overcoming any obstacle that would hinder the possibility of this existence altogether. For some, it would be very easy to support this fact as we can see the expected ways a man should handle the different situations that he is faced with every day. Men were taught that crying is a sense of weakness, that not being the head of the household, even when he's jobless, is a clear indication that he has failed the family. He was brought up to think that sitting on the toilet to urinate means his feminine side has dominated its role. And do not forget that if a man dares to speak of the pain he is currently undergoing, that simply means he needs to go back to end of the line and once more wait his turn for his second chance of being created.

We understand that you were all taught that these things are what makes you less of the man you are but it should not be that because of your woes, a woman must suffer the many blows of your hands. If you are victims of societal misjudgment, isn't it true that you should now become the protectors of your opposites? Isn't it true that you must now do everything in your power to make sure a woman is protected from all of this? Will not the change you make, and the cycle you break, be a clear indication that you are the ones standing up and fighting for an ending to this societal bondage that seems to be the mastermind behind the ruins of your sought identities. If you are our leaders, why do we have to end up in an ongoing fight to make a way for ourselves?

About the Author

Sherene Mckoy is an enthusiastic, Jamaican mother of one from the eccentric city of Spanish Town. She is a multi-passionate woman who is gifted in songwriting and interior decorating. Being the ninth sibling from a family of ten, she knew that nothing in life would come easy; nothing would be given to her on a silver platter. She was always certain of one thing- she loved putting words on paper, especially because of its therapeutic benefits.

Though groomed in a loving home by married parents, she wrestled with the realities of broken homes and single parent families. Her personal experience in relationships magnified some unhealthy patterns in the lives of women and the reasons for their recurrence. This book was written to reflect the shared experiences of herself and fellow sisters, experiences of which a common denominator was hurt inflicted by men. This book was an outlet to comfort herself and other women who may have unfairly blamed themselves for failed relationships. She aims to expose in an effort to caution women and hopefully, inspire change in men who display similar traits to the men in these stories.

GLOSSARY

Word/Phrase	Description
A	
Am	I am
A *mad* yuh a get mad?	Are you going crazy/mad?
A chuu	It's true
Agoh	Going to
A wah dis?	What is this?
A wah?	What is it?
A wah a gwaan ya soh!	What's going on here?
Agen	Again
Awrite, si di food here	Alright, here is the food
A chuu mi nuh have	It's because I don't have
Whole-a	A whole
B	
Bout	About
'Bring in the bread'	To make money

By the time yuh quint	Quickly/rapidly
Butsiya!	An expression expressing shock and disbelief
Bwoy fren	Boyfriend
Bad man	Dangerous man
Bawl	Cry
Bap, bap!	An expression of excitement
Bredda	Brother
C	
Chat	Talk
Coolie	Jamaican Indian or someone who is of East Indian descent
Cuz!	Cousin
Crosses	Misfortune
Crocodile tears	Excessive crying
Cover his tracks	Conceal evidence of one's activities
Could-a mean	Could have meant
Cos	Because
D	
Dis	This
Dat	That
Di	The
Dis	This

Dem a sleep	They are sleeping
E	
Enuh!	You know!
Ediat	Idiot/Stupid
F	
Fi	For
Farin	Foreign
Fada	Father
Fah	For
Frenemies faasing in his business'	Enemies prying for information
Fight 'gainst	Fight against
Fi mi	My/mine
Fus	First
G	
Get a work a farin	Gain employment overseas
Gyal	Girl
Gud	Good
Gud mawning	Good morning
Greater Portmore	One of the communities in Portmore, Jamaica
Girl chile, is what?!"	My child, what is it?

H	
Him use mi back	He used me again
Har	Her
I	
Is only U.S. mi have	I only have US dollars
Inna	Into
J	
Jus' a goh cool out likkle bit	Just going to get a little fresh air
Jamdung	Jamaica/Jamaican
K	
Kip	Keep
L	
Likkle	Little
Luk	Look
Lef	Leave
Luv	Love
M	
Missa	Mr.
Mi	Me
Mada	Mother

May God guh wid yuh	May God go with you
Mi wi dweet	I will do it
Mi chile	My child
Minding him pickney dem	Providing for his children
Mi never waah jinx it	I didn't want to bring back luck to it
Mi deh yah	I am here
Matta	Matter
Miself	Myself
Mi nuh inna dem yah slackness ya, enuh!	I will not tolerate this slackness!
Mi nuh inna weh yuh inna!"	I will not be an accomplice/ I will not be a part of it
Mi nuh have nuttin fi tell har seh!"	I have nothing to tell her
Mi wi dweet	I will do it
N	
Nuhbadi nuh deh home	There is nobody home
Nuttin	Nothing
Nuh got on nuh	Don't have on an
nuhbady	Nobody
O	

Ounu man nuh easy at all	You men are interesting
P	
Pay mi fi di balance	Pay me any outstanding money owed
Pon	On
Pickney dem	Children
'People place'	Rent house
"Putting dat likkle coolie gyal"	Putting that little coolie girl
R	
Rispek	Respect
S	
Shack up	To live together as spouses without being legally married
Suppen	Something
Show bad face	Give an attitude
Sick to mi stomach	Disgusted
Seh	Say
Sar	Sir
Soh stop mope around like smaddy dead	Desist from being depressed/downtrodden
Seh something!"	Say something

Shi carry yuh off!	She enhances you/ She makes you look good
Si	See
T	
Tail pon fire	Enthusiastic, excited, or passionate about something
t'ree pickney	Three children
Tek care a yuhself	Take care of yourself
Ting	Thing
Togedda	Together
Tink	Think
Tell lie on sickness	Pretend to be sick/ pretend that someone is sick
Tell mi!	Tell me
U	
Unno	You all
V	
Vice	Voice
W	
Waan	Want to
Weh yuh a…?	Why did you…?
Wok fi yuh	Work for you
We yuh jus come out a	That you just came out of

Weh yuh seh?	What did you say?
Weh dem deh	Where are they?
Why yuh never tell wi seh yuh comin?"	Why didn't you tell me that you were coming?
Whore	A prostitute.
Wid	With
What di hell!	A phrase/reaction to something strange/abnormal to the person
Working under the table	Unreported employment
Would-a	Would have
Wi	Us
Where a mus	Where must I
Wanda	Wonder
Y	
Yuh	You
Yuh si	You see
yuh aguh mek it	You will make it
"Yuh ok, idawta?"	Are you OK my daughter?
Yuh did a plan dis!"	You were planning this!
Yuh gone a lead now!	Gone ahead of the rest
Yaad	Yard

Made in United States
Orlando, FL
15 June 2023

33993241R00182